"I tore through this in one evening and didn't
to read, and packed with clever strategies, Jes. ~ quick start guide is a
fantastic place to start for anyone looking to better understand their—or a
loved one's—ADHD."

— JESSICA MCCABE, author of *How to ADHD: An Insider's Guide to Working with Your Brain (Not Against It)*

"I've read tons of ADHD books—or, more accurately, I've started tons of
them—but Jesse's is legit the first one I've actually finished (and I did
it in one sitting). *Extra Focus* is an entertaining and incredibly easy read,
with no unnecessary repetition for the sake of extra pages. Just concise
information and practical tips, sprinkled with tons of relatable 'ohhhh,
it's not just me!' moments. I really wish this guide existed when I first got
diagnosed. If you're dealing with ADHD—or even just trying to understand
it better—I highly recommend you check out *Extra Focus*. Trust me (and
thank Jesse later)."

— DANI DONOVAN, ADHD creator and author of *The Anti-Planner: How to Get Sh*t Done When You Don't Feel Like It*

"Critical insights on ADHD and actionable strategies to deal with it.
Wonderfully describes and simplifies the concept."

— DEREK SIVERS, author, founder, sive.rs

"I've been waiting for Jesse Anderson to get all his ideas down in a book. His
newsletter and tweets have improved my life so much. He gets the ADHD
brain better than anyone I've seen and offers usable, smart tools and the
context to make me interested in them. I'm so glad he has put all of that
in one place, because I have ADHD and am not good at looking in lots of
different places."

— ADAM DAVIDSON, cofounder of NPR's *Planet Money* podcast and
author of *The Passion Economy*

PRAISE FOR *EXTRA FOCUS*

"There's a reason hundreds of thousands of people on social media have been drawn to Jesse J. Anderson's thoughts around ADHD: he's better at combining first-hand experiences with well-researched facts than just about anybody. *Extra Focus* is a compelling read for those who have wondered why they just can't focus the way other people can. Packed with strategies, anecdotes and revelations, it's a must-read on the topic."

— ANNA DAVID, New York Times bestselling author

"*Extra Focus* is chock full of smart, practical advice and strategies with the perfect amount of tongue-in-cheek honesty—the Jesse J. Anderson special—sprinkled throughout. It's a must read for every ADHDer out there, regardless of where you are on your journey. You'll learn something new, I promise!"

— LINDSAY GUENTZEL, host & producer of *Refocused, A Podcast All About ADHD*

"This book was what I needed when I was first diagnosed with ADHD as an adult in my thirties. Jesse has a natural knack for making the reader feel both seen and validated in their ADHD experiences - something that's needed in the ADHD space. His non-judgmental, relatable insights will be so valuable to someone who is just discovering their ADHD or suspects that they might be neurodivergent. The strategies in this book have changed the way that I look at my symptoms - giving me more confidence and tools to not only survive through ADHD, but to actually be proud of the strengths that I have as an ADHDer."

— TRINA HAYNES, ADHD creator and founder of *My Lady ADHD*

"Jesse has always been a fantastic resource on social media for me, and no surprise, his book is no different. It's perfect for the newly diagnosed ADHDer and gives helpful perspective and valuable information to just about anyone."

— **RON CAPALBO,** ADHD coach, advocate, and speaker

"Welcome to your next hyperfocus - an ADHD-friendly guide to making friends with your brain! A must-read for any ADHD-er."

— **LEANNE MASKELL,** founder & CEO of *ADHD Works*, author of *ADHD: an A to Z*

EXTRA FOCUS

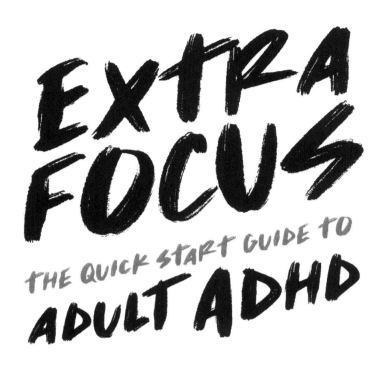

EXTRA FOCUS
THE QUICK START GUIDE TO ADULT ADHD

JESSE J. ANDERSON

ILLUSTRATED BY NATE KADLAC

VADA PRESS
Puyallup, Washington

Library of Congress Control Number: 2023917486

Extra Focus ISBNs:

979-8-9886442-0-0   paperback
979-8-9886442-1-7   ebook

Produced by Jesse J. Anderson
Cover design by Jesse J. Anderson

Editing by Adam Rosen
Illustrations by Nate Kadlac

Published by Vada Press

Special discount available for bulk sales.
Please contact bulksales@adhdjesse.com

adhdjesse.com

To everyone who was told they were just lazy.

Contents

THIS BOOK COMES WITH FREE BONUS MATERIAL

Visit **extrafocusbook.com/bonus** to access:

Discussion / Reflection Questions
ADHD Motivation Cheat Sheet
ADHD Strategies Reference
ADHD Resources Guide

Intro

When I was thirty-six years old, I found out that I had Attention-Deficit/Hyperactivity Disorder. Or, as most people know it, ADHD.

My friend Brian (not his real name) had been diagnosed a few months earlier. Our wives were talking about it one day, and my wife realized his symptoms could have just as easily been describing me.

She suggested I might want to look into it, but I insisted I couldn't have ADHD. "I have no problem focusing on things I'm interested in," I said. Because I believed I already knew what ADHD was, I assumed people with ADHD couldn't focus at all.

Our conversation stayed in the back of my mind, however, and eventually I started doing research on ADHD to find out if I could see in myself what my wife saw. I do love a good investigation.

Pretty quickly, I discovered that people with ADHD have no problem focusing on things they're interested in. In fact, hyperfocus is a common symptom of ADHD. It's when you focus so intently on something interesting that you lose track of everything else.

Hmm. That sounded familiar.

I had always thought ADHD was a label for the hyperactive boy who couldn't sit still or focus for more than two seconds. The kid that chased squirrels and bounced off the walls. But that version of ADHD didn't sound much like me, so I assumed I couldn't have it.

As I continued to read about ADHD, though, I kept seeing myself over and over. So many of my "personality quirks" turned out to be extremely common in people with ADHD:

- the way I struggled with motivation
- the way I constantly started new hobbies, only to abandon them soon after
- the way I was always late to everything, no matter how hard I tried
- the way new and interesting things constantly distracted me
- the way I often forgot small but important details
- the way I was extremely sensitive to rejection
- the way boredom felt absolutely excruciating
- the way my emotions often felt intense and beyond my control
- the way I procrastinated on anything that wasn't immediately gratifying or fun

It turned out I really didn't have a clue what ADHD was. The more I read, the clearer it became that ADHD was the missing key to unlocking why my brain worked the way it did.

It was the reason every teacher said I was "gifted" but wasn't reaching my potential, or I was "a joy to have in class" but kept getting in my own way. Or why I had been called lazy, crazy, spacey, stupid, selfish, and other terrible names for a child to hear. Words used by adults and authority figures to describe my behavior, as if the way I acted was a willful act of disobedience.

But those words never rang true for me. They didn't describe the person I thought I was.

I was often ashamed of the way my brain worked and how my actions never seemed to line up with my intentions. I was also confused. Over the years, the questions "What were you thinking?!" and "What is *wrong* with you?!" were all too frequently directed my way. And honestly, I didn't have a great answer.

As a child, I knew I wanted to do good. I wanted friends to like me, I wanted to please my parents and teachers, and I wanted to get good grades.

It was the same as an adult. I wanted to do good work. I wanted coworkers and peers to like me, I wanted to please my parents and those who employed me, and I wanted to create great things and get stuff done.

Sometimes those things would happen! Something unlocked inside me, and I would be extremely productive. I would impress others with a creative or unique approach to solving a problem or accomplish a week's worth of work on a lone Saturday afternoon.

But more often than not, I would get stuck on a single problem for hours or even days. I would avoid simple tasks, all the while screaming at my brain to "Just do the thing!" Like clockwork, at the end of each day I'd wonder where the time had gone and why so many tasks were still unfinished.

Now I understand I kept running into these difficulties because I have a different type of brain—a brain with ADHD. For a long time, I didn't know how that brain worked, what motivated it, or why I couldn't focus on things that were extremely important (even if they were also boring). I didn't understand why my actions so often went against my own intentions. Why I seemed to work against myself.

Once I was diagnosed with ADHD, I learned so much more about how my brain worked. And the more I learned about it, the more that many of the challenges I'd had in my life seemed to make sense.

It didn't solve or excuse any of the difficulties I often faced, but it gave me an explanation for why my brain worked the way it did. Why my immediate reactions often got me into trouble. Why "trying harder" didn't work. Why people said I had "such great potential," which always seemed just out of reach.

This knowledge allowed me to forgive myself for the areas where I fell short of other people's standards—and my own. It gave me a new perspective on how my brain worked, pushing me toward a better way to live.

Most importantly, though, it gave me hope. I now knew my brain worked differently than most, which led me to discover proven ways to minimize my challenges and take advantage of my unique strengths. Yes, my life may be different than others', but it doesn't need to be any less enriching.

If you're new to understanding ADHD, this quick start guide will help deepen your base of knowledge and teach you how to thrive with Adult ADHD. If you're already familiar with the ins and outs of ADHD, it will feel familiar in some ways but will also offer new insights and strategies to help you put your knowledge into practice.

Wherever you're coming from, it will help you view life with ADHD from a fresh perspective. You'll learn practical motivation strategies that are crafted to harmonize with your brain. You'll understand—maybe for the first time—why your brain works the way it does and how to thrive within your circumstances.

Best of all, it will help you live a less stressful, more rewarding life as an adult with ADHD.

Ready to get started? You got this.

UNRAVELING THE ADHD MIND

What Is ADHD?

ADHD has a PR problem: most people have heard of it, but most people don't actually know what it is. The confusion starts with its name.

ADHD is a terrible name.

To start, "Attention-Deficit/Hyperactivity Disorder" carries a lot of unfortunate baggage. Far from clarifying the many myths out there about ADHD, the name itself perpetuates many of them. It's confusing and misleading.

You may have heard the name and thought, "I can't have ADHD, I'm not hyperactive!" or "I can't have ADHD, I have *plenty* of attention for the things that interest me." As I mentioned earlier, for most of my life it had never occurred to me I could have ADHD, either. If the name was more accurate, could I have been diagnosed earlier in life? It's definitely a possibility.

Let's take a few moments to dissect the name further.

Attention Deficit

Those of us with ADHD don't actually have a deficit of attention. It's the opposite—we have an abundance of it! We're often paying attention to everything all at once; so much so that we can lose track of what's important.

We get bombarded by all the incoming signals, paying so much attention to all that we see and hear around us that we can't regulate the flood of data to focus on what should matter most.

The things that should be most important (the person talking to us, the project we're working on, the signals our body sends us to eat, drink, or go to the bathroom) often get lost in the noise.

Rather than characterizing those with ADHD as having an attention *deficit*, it would be far more accurate to say they have a *dysregulation* of attention.

When everything is shouting for your attention, it's difficult to regulate that attention and pick a specific voice out of the noise.

Hyperactivity

While some people with ADHD are noticeably hyperactive, many are not. This is particularly true for women, who are less likely to present symptoms of being hyperactive, at least outwardly.[1] Many people think they can't possibly have ADHD because they assume external hyperactivity is a required symptom. Who can blame them—*it's right there in the name!*

But hyperactivity is only one way ADHD can present itself.

Some people with ADHD say they experience hyperactivity more on the inside of their brain, even when they seem perfectly calm from the outside.

Maybe you're a fast talker, or someone who fidgets, doodles, or bounces your leg when sitting—all ways of working out that internal hyperactivity. Perhaps you feel like your brain is constantly racing, juggling forty-seven ideas at once, always chasing down a new thought, and then another one, and another one. But those feelings don't present outwardly in a way others can see.

You don't "look" hyperactive, so the name doesn't seem to fit.

Disorder

Words like disorder, disability, and deficit often carry a negative and stigmatized connotation. This is mostly because of ableism—the societal prejudice that casts "disability" and related words as something undesirable.

Because of this, many choose to embrace more positive or strengths-based language. For example, they might refer to ADHD as a brain *difference* rather than disorder.

This can be a touchy subject, so let's tackle both sides of it.

On one hand, some people think of their ADHD as a "super-power," leaning into the different way their brain works and embracing those differences as a strength. In the right context, some attributes of ADHD can absolutely feel like a superpower!

People with ADHD can flourish and get amazing work done when they have a job that encourages creativity or urgency, particularly in industries like entertainment, emergency services, marketing, entrepreneurship, software development, writing, etc.

At times, the unique way my brain works has felt like a strength for me too.

In urgent crisis situations, I am at my best! If you want to brainstorm some creative new ideas—I'm your guy.

On the other hand, if you want someone who can accurately fill out time sheets or hand in their expense reports on time, you best look elsewhere. Not just because I hate that kind of work (which I do). But because that work feels literally impossible for me. My brain doesn't work the same way as most people, which makes it especially challenging to complete certain types of tasks.

During times where my ADHD brain feels more like a hindrance than an asset, it makes sense that the way my brain works would be called a "disorder." That label may come with a negative connotation, but I mean it in a neutral, matter-of-fact way.

The bottom line is that under certain circumstances, it is more difficult for me to function or successfully fulfill a role than it would be for someone with a typical type of brain.

Three Presentations of ADHD

Since ADHD looks different for different people, healthcare professionals use categories, called presentations, to group people with ADHD who experience similar symptoms. This can help with diagnosis and more effective treatment plans.

There are three different presentations of ADHD: predominantly inattentive, predominantly hyperactive-impulsive, and combined presentation. These labels come from the *Diagnostic and Statistical Manual of Mental Disorders*, or DSM, the standardized reference manual developed by mental health professionals in the United States.

The first edition of the DSM was published in 1952; the most recent edition, DSM-5-TR, in 2022. Because the DSM is the authoritative handbook for the fields of psychology and psychiatry, it provides professionals with a common language for diagnosing ADHD and a list of symptoms for each presentation.

ADHD Presentation Symptoms

The list of symptoms for each presentation that follows is not intended to be a self-diagnosis tool, but it's helpful to know what doctors and medical professionals may look for (and which presentation you may fall under).

Here are the symptoms for each presentation based on the definitions in the DSM-5-TR. (They've been lightly edited for clarity.)

PREDOMINANTLY INATTENTIVE PRESENTATION

- ☐ Fails to pay close attention to details or makes careless mistakes
- ☐ Has trouble holding attention
- ☐ Does not seem to listen when spoken to directly
- ☐ Has trouble following through on instructions
- ☐ Has trouble organizing tasks and activities
- ☐ Avoids, dislikes, or is reluctant to do tasks requiring sustained mental effort
- ☐ Loses things necessary for tasks and activities
- ☐ Easily distracted
- ☐ Forgetful in daily activities

PREDOMINANTLY HYPERACTIVE-IMPULSIVE PRESENTATION

☐ Fidgets with or taps hands or feet, or squirms in seat

☐ Has trouble remaining seated

☐ Runs or climbs in inappropriate situations as a child; feels restless as an adult

☐ Unable to take part in leisure activities quietly (e.g., watching TV)

☐ Constantly acts or feels "on the go" or as if "driven by a motor"

☐ Talks excessively

☐ Blurts out answers before a question has been completed

☐ Has trouble waiting their turn

☐ Interrupts or intrudes on others

COMBINED PRESENTATION

☐ Meets criteria for both inattentive and hyperactive-impulsive presentations

Knowing Your Presentation

According to the DSM-5-TR, the criterion for an adult diagnosis of ADHD is to have five or more symptoms of either inattentive or hyperactive-impulsive presentation or five or more of both (combined presentation). For a diagnosis in children, six or more symptoms must be exhibited.

In addition, your symptoms or behaviors must have persisted for six or more months, been present in two or more settings (home, work, school, etc.), and some symptoms should have been present before the age of twelve.

It's important to understand that someone's presentation can change; that's why they're called "presentations" of ADHD, not "types" of ADHD. They represent how your ADHD currently presents itself, i.e., which of your symptoms are most visible.

For example, someone with a predominantly hyperactive-impulsive presentation as a child may "mellow out" over time, leading to a combined or inattentive presentation as an adult. Their diagnosis didn't change—it's still just ADHD. But the way it presents itself has changed.

What the DSM-5-TR Doesn't Cover

The symptom lists in the DSM enable medical professionals to diagnose ADHD, and they can be helpful for non-professionals to understand some of the more easily recognizable signs of ADHD. But they are missing a lot of important nuances about what it's actually like to live with ADHD.

They don't explore issues like motivation, hyperfocus, emotional dysregulation, rejection sensitivity, time management, and memory deficits. As you'll discover in the sections to come, there's a lot more to ADHD than the DSM-5-TR would seem to show.

Managing Your Attention

I'm sitting at a coffee shop and working on my laptop when an old friend enters.

She notices me and walks over to say hello. I momentarily break focus from my screen to return the greeting and we strike up a conversation.

After a few minutes of chatting, my attention starts to drift away. My friend is still talking, but I'm thinking about that project open on my laptop. Also, a child nearby just bumped his head and is looking around to see if he should start crying. A barista complains to a coworker about a speeding ticket. And is that couple sitting by the front window breaking up?

I find myself wondering if that brick wall in the corner is made of real bricks or just one of those fake panels. If it is fake, it's a good fake. I wonder how it would look in my office. A brick wall in the office . . . that would be cool. On the West Coast, brick walls are still cool.

Suddenly, I realize my friend has stopped talking and looks offended.

What happened?

Even though I knew it was important to pay attention to the conversation, my focus drifted anyway. I wanted to pay attention. I value my friends and would never intentionally leave them feeling neglected. But at some point, my brain just couldn't ignore all the other "interesting" things happening in the room.

I didn't even know I was distracted until it was too late.

Your Attention Assistant

At any given moment, your brain absorbs an enormous amount of information.

To make sense of all that incoming data, your brain makes split-second calculations to decide which data is important and which can be ignored. It's almost like your brain has an attention assistant in charge of gathering and sorting all the signals around you.

When I was in that coffee shop, besides my friend's voice, my attention assistant was busy detecting:

- the sounds of conversations happening around us
- the sweet aroma of my caramel macchiato and roasting coffee beans
- the sight of the child bumping their head
- the feeling of my fingers still resting on the keyboard
- and a hundred more things happening all around me

The attention assistant takes in all that information and tells your conscious brain what to pay attention to.

For someone without ADHD, the attention assistant sorts through that mountain of data and determines which things are important and which aren't. Then they deliver a nice, sorted stack of the most important information to the desk of your conscious brain.

All those distractions happening in the coffee shop get tossed in the trash, so your conscious brain ignores them, remaining focused on what matters: the conversation with your friend.

But when you have ADHD, your attention assistant rarely knows which data is important and which to ignore. Rather than getting a neat, curated stack of only the most important data, you get dumped with every last bit of information. Even the unimportant stuff. You're left to process an unsorted, unfiltered, giant mess of information.

Your brain doesn't know what to focus on among the mess, so it tries to focus on everything at the same time. Or when that fails—which it will—it starts to just pick the most interesting or colorful things from the pile, focusing on the shiniest rather than the most important. You become so hyperfocused on this that you forget about everything else.

You know that paying attention to your conversation is important. But there's so much data coming in that your brain lost track of the conversation and got distracted by something else. It's almost like your brain has become overwhelmed with all the constant data, so when it finds something interesting, it ignores everything else entirely. Your focus narrows to that single thing, which may or may not be important.

Hyperfocus

Growing up, I always knew I could intensely focus on things I was interested in.

Whether it was playing video games, reading science-fiction, learning web design, organizing trading cards, or some other nerdy hobby . . . I could spend hours in these worlds.

I wasn't just focused. I was *hyper*focused. So focused that other signals couldn't reach me.

Food?
Sleep?
Alarms?
Appointments?
Bathroom breaks?
Someone yelling my name?
The sense of time passing me by?

When I was hyperfocused, none of those got through.

Eventually, at some point, I would snap out of my spell. Those signals had been collecting in a queue, waiting for me to realize they were there. Suddenly, I'd find myself sprinting to the bathroom, apologizing to someone, or swearing at myself for missing something important. Again.

Hyperfocus vs. Flow State

Hyperfocus is similar to another concept called flow state.

A flow state occurs when someone becomes fully engaged and immersed in an activity. It often happens when there is a perfect alignment of challenge and skill level. Many people refer to it as "being in the zone," that moment when you're performing at your best and getting things done with ease.

In a flow state, you may find yourself thinking (and believing), "I can't be stopped!" Crucially, though, you can redirect your focus to whatever task needs to be done.

In *hyperfocus*, on the other hand, you feel more like you're stuck. There's one direct line of focus between you and whatever you're hyperfocused on. You may think, "I can't stop!" You're afraid that if you try to redirect your focus anywhere else, you'll disrupt your momentum and never get it back.

With hyperfocus, there's often a feeling of compulsion and completionism. Worried you'll never have this motivation again or may forget the task if you hit pause, you feel you must keep going until you've accomplished whatever it is you think you need to do. This can be productive when you're focused on a project that is urgent, but less so when focused on something that ultimately isn't important.

When you're hyperfocused on something, it often feels like the most important thing you could be doing. You may even make deals with yourself—I'll eat after I finish this section, I'll shower after one more time—afraid it'll all be over once you stop.

But once you finally do stop, you often realize the thing you were hyperfocused on wasn't that important after all. It was merely a tangent that felt impossible to ignore in the moment. After all, did you *really* need to spend two hours researching optimal shoelace lengths? Probably not.

Tangents You Can't Ignore

I'm a software developer, and sometimes when I'm working on a project I get hyperfocused on one minor detail that's ultimately not that important. I might try to build a new page for an app and consider the different options for how to style a button. And hey, maybe I can build a solution that lets me reuse this button and swap out the colors or the font or the size of the button or a million other custom features.

Soon, eight hours have gone by, the page isn't done, and I have an entire, elaborate button *system* even though I only needed a single button.

Maybe your hyperfocus tangents have left you with a pointlessly reorganized bookshelf, an extensive research project you'll never look at again, or a perfectly sorted collection of Lego blocks—color-coordinated and all—only to eventually be dumped back into a single giant bin.

On the flip side, when hyperfocus is at its best, you can be super productive.

You might have been avoiding an important project or school paper for the last four weeks, but suddenly the urgency of tomorrow's deadline sends you to hyperfocus. You work at 10x speed and finish the entire thing in one (sleepless) night.

But even this "productive" version of hyperfocus can cause you trouble. It may give you unrealistic expectations about your performance and ability to get things done. You won't always be moving at 10x speed, so your normal work-load may make you feel you are falling short of your potential. (That cursed word again—*potential*.)

When you've experienced productive hyperfocus, you may think that level of productivity is your norm and anything less is a failure.

Another problem with hyperfocus is that people see you focused intensely on one thing, which makes them think you can control your focus. They might say, "You don't seem to have a problem focusing on video games" or "If you really wanted to, you could focus on this important but boring task."

Your tendency toward distraction may seem to be an act of defiance or selfishness. Or worse, laziness.

But that's simply not true. You can't control your focus through sheer will. You can't coerce it, no matter how important the task, how much someone else wants you to focus on it, or even how much *you* want to focus on it.

Instead, we're far better off when we understand what drives our brains to stay focused, what motivates us. This knowledge lets you lean into your strength so you can, in the words of Jessica McCabe, "work with your brain, not against it."[2]

MOTIVATION

Motivating the ADHD Brain

One of the biggest struggles of having ADHD is finding motivation.

The problem is that everyone expects you to be motivated by the same things that motivate others. Even you expect to be motivated by these things. It can be baffling when this doesn't seem to work.

One common solution is to research and implement the latest productivity tips and tricks. But, if you're anything like me, you ultimately run into frustration when nothing seems to stick or work for longer than a day or two.

So you end up with a graveyard of earnest but ill-guided attempts. Abandoned to-do apps with complicated systems you thought would be helpful, or stacks and stacks of beautiful planners with only a few marked-up pages.

These systems rarely work because they weren't designed for your brain. You need a new approach—one that takes into account how the ADHD brain works. (More on this in a moment.)

Most people (often called neurotypical people) are motivated primarily by three key factors: **importance, rewards, and consequences**. When something is important, they move it to the top of their to-do list. The same goes for tasks with significant rewards or consequences. Most productivity strategies and systems are built with this in mind.

This can lead people with ADHD into believing three big myths about how motivation works for us.

ADHD Motivation Myths

1. If something is **important** to you, you will do it.
2. Increasing a **reward** will increase your motivation.
3. Harsher **consequences** will give you more willpower.

We do often know when things are important. When they are, we *want* to do them. But that doesn't actually provide motivation.

Rewards and consequences that are *immediate* can sometimes motivate, but delayed rewards don't really motivate us at all. We can't simply "try harder" and force these things to work. We need to approach our motivation in a different way, a way that is compatible with our brain.

Specifically, one of the greatest challenges we face is task initiation—actually getting started on a task. Moving thought into action.

Dr. William Dodson, a board-certified psychiatrist who was one of the first practitioners to specialize in treating adults with ADHD, suggests people with ADHD have a different nervous system than neurotypical people. He theorizes that while most people have an **importance**-based nervous system, people with ADHD have an **interest**-based nervous system. They primarily find motivation through interest, novelty, challenge, and urgency.

Even if you haven't heard of the interest-based nervous system, reading about it right now might make immediate sense to you. If you have ADHD, you've surely struggled with finding motivation for things that are really important, like that big project or paper that's due next month.

But you may have had no trouble finding motivation to explore some interesting new hobby, or solving a puzzle others said was impossible, or working on that big project once it becomes urgent.

I've spent many late nights working on something that I had weeks (or even months) to work on, waiting until the due date is the next day to finally find the motivation to get started. (And that's often when I do my best work.)

The news isn't all bad, though. When we know what motivates our brain, we can use that knowledge to help with task initiation, our biggest motivation-related difficulty.

This is where the 4 Cs come in. They are a set of easy-to-remember prompts to help you get motivated and reset, no matter how far behind or overwhelmed you are.

The 4 Cs

- Captivate (interest)
- Create (novelty)
- Compete (challenge)
- Complete (urgency)

When you're stuck with a task you can't seem to get started on, use these to initiate or spark you into action. It might not be immediately obvious how to do this, so let's look at some examples to help get you into the right mindset.

Putting the 4 Cs into Action

Let's take something most people hate to do: washing dishes.

Washing dishes is the worst. My brain hates it—it's boring, monotonous, and mundane. It's important (just ask my wife), but not very fun or exciting.

It's a chore that doesn't seem to have anything for our interest-focused brain. No real challenge (other than getting started), nothing captivating or interesting about it, zero creativity or novelty, and it often never becomes truly urgent. You could always buy paper plates, quickly rinse a dish when you need it, or maybe even just use a paper towel. (I've done it, you've probably done it—desperate times call for desperate measures).

So how can we find motivation for this boring chore? Let's go through each of the 4 Cs and see how they could be applied in this scenario.

CAPTIVATE: MAKE DOING THE DISHES INTERESTING

You probably won't ever find doing the dishes interesting or captivating. But maybe there's a new hobby you're really into, and you can find a good podcast or audiobook on that topic. You can save that podcast or book to listen to only when doing the dishes. That way, the task goes from "doing the dishes" to "listening to your favorite podcast." The dishes become just something you busy yourself with while you listen.

CREATE: MAKE DOING THE DISHES NOVEL

There are a lot of simple ways of making doing the dishes feel more novel. Many of these ideas may sound silly at first, but they really can make it easier to find the motivation you need to get started. One idea is to unload the dishes to your kitchen table first, put them into stacks, and then move those stacks to the cupboards. Or maybe you could load the dishwasher alphabetically: start with bowls, then move on to cups, forks, knives, plates, spoons, etc. These little tweaks can make a boring task just a bit more novel, which can tickle your brain just enough to get you started.

COMPETE: MAKE DOING THE DISHES A FUN CHALLENGE

Set a timer and see how quickly you can gather all the dirty dishes around your kitchen, dining room, office, bathroom, car . . . you know, the normal places people collect dirty dishes. Race with a partner or even a friend over the phone. Text each other when you're starting on the task and see who

finishes loading their dishwasher first. Ignite that internal desire to win (and celebrate each other for taking on the task).

COMPLETE: MAKE DOING THE DISHES URGENT

Creating urgency is often about creating deadlines that feel nearly imminent. Maybe you queue up your favorite nightly show but aren't allowed to watch it until you've finished loading the dishwasher. Or maybe simply setting a timer can be enough to move you into action and introduce that urgency.

Look for Strategies That Work for Now (Not Forever)

An important note: these methods won't always work! That's okay and expected.

We aren't looking for a strategy that is going to **solve** doing the dishes. We are just looking for potential strategies that can work for the current moment. When they don't work, they don't work—so we move on and try something new. We can always come back to try them again later.

Our brains are always looking for novelty, so we will need to switch these strategies up a lot. They may work great for a week and then fall flat the next. When that happens, you can use the 4 Cs approach to create a new strategy.

When you feel you're stuck on the couch, unable to move yourself into action—think about how you can Captivate, Create, Compete, or Complete to start that task and get moving.

4 Cs Template

The 4 Cs are a handy template to help you put your motivation into gear. Before you start something, ask yourself the following questions:

- **Captivate:** how can I make it interesting?
- **Create:** how can I make it creative or novel?
- **Compete:** how can I make it competitive or challenging?
- **Complete:** how can I make its completion feel urgent?

Here's the formula:

> *To get started on **[important task/project]**, I can use **[captivate, create, compete, complete]** to ignite my motivation and build momentum.*

Building Your Motivation Momentum

The 4 Cs are a great way to get started on a specific task you're stuck on. But they can also build up your momentum for getting lots of other things done.

Living with ADHD is often about managing your productive energy. Think of your motivation like a train. On one hand, it's incredibly powerful, and once it's moving it can be impossible to stop. On the other hand, it starts off motionless and intimidatingly heavy, and it can often feel impossible to get moving at all.

Here's the thing, though: a train doesn't move everything in one motion. That would be an impossible task. It might have dozens of cars—maybe even a hundred or more—far too much weight to start everything moving at once.

Instead, it starts by powering just an engine or two. The engine pulls a single car, and then another car, and another. As the engine continues moving forward and building speed, the coupler between each car tightens one by one, until eventually 12,000 tons of cargo are being pulled by the engine and the entire train is moving at top speed.

So when we try to move the entire train at once, it's no wonder we so often get stuck in place.

One of the most popular bits of productivity advice is to "eat the frog first." In other words, when you're working on something, you should tackle the hardest tasks before the easier ones. Seems reasonable. But this advice is toxic for the ADHD brain!

It might sound logical that if you tackle the hardest problem first, the rest of the day will be easier. But the reality never seems to line up. The difficult task is often too much to confront before building up any momentum, so we end up staring at it all day and get nothing done at all.

Or maybe we spend the day researching frogs or trains instead—anything to avoid that task we really, *really* don't want to do.

The weight is just too much. At the end of the day, you're stuck in place, exerting effort but getting nowhere. Spinning your wheels.

That massive weight is the force of resistance, the friction that gets in our way. We're always going to be facing that resistance, so we need to build up momentum to push past it. The best way to do this is to muster up just enough positive momentum to start, one step at a time, until those harder tasks become less daunting.

So don't try to eat the frog first: **eat the ice cream first!**

Rather than starting with that big, ugly task you don't want to do, find small (and fun!) tasks that naturally align with the Captivate, Create, Compete, Complete approach and start your day with those. **Don't save the fun tasks for last. Use them to get yourself moving down the track.** Make that incremental progress. Build momentum.

Once you're moving and gaining speed, those hard tasks won't feel as impossible anymore.

You may have experienced this phenomenon by accident. Maybe you worked on something fun and easy, got into a groove, and suddenly found yourself using that momentum to tackle some herculean task, a task you couldn't get started on before, no matter what tip or trick you threw at it.

Once that train is moving at top speed, nothing can stop you.

Developing Habits and Routines

One great paradox of having ADHD is your relationship with structure. It's essential to help us manage our lives, yet we have a strong tendency to resist it.

I know I need it, but structure just feels so confining!

I worry it will feel like a bunch of rules that, once set, will keep me from being able to do the things I want to do. I want to be able to be spontaneous. I want to seek out things that are interesting or novel, even if they weren't what I had planned to do. Adding structure and rules for managing my life feels like a loss of control.

The idea of imposing structure might make us feel this way. But we have to wrestle with reality: without systems and routines, our lives can quickly fall into disarray. We bounce from one thing to the next, never quite accomplishing any of the goals we set out to achieve.

So if we want to work in synergy with our brains, we have to tackle structure head-on. We can do this by working with our brain's natural rhythm. The systems and routines we use should feel empowering rather than limiting.

To that end, we can avoid the constricting feeling of structure by building around positive habits.

Take reward-seeking. If I do the dishes and my wife gives me a kiss and tells me, "Great job!" I'm going to be a lot more likely to repeat that behavior! The next time I think about the dishes, I'll remember the positive vibes I got the last time I did them, which makes me more likely to get to work.

That encouragement creates a positive feedback loop. You take a positive action, get some sort of positive result, and teach your brain that this is a good thing to do. It's that simple.

Think of the mouse getting its cheese at the end of a maze. The first time you put it in the maze, it wanders around slowly, not sure where to go. But once it discovers there's a highly desirable treat at the end of the maze, it wants to run the maze again and again. Soon you drop the mouse into the maze and it doesn't even hesitate; it sprints right to the finish line. Eventually, you don't even need the cheese to get it motivated.

That's what you want to do with your routines. They should feel second-nature, so you don't even know you're engaged in a routine. You're just doing something you usually do, without thinking about it.

What gets rewarded gets repeated. If we want to create a routine that will stick, we want to make sure we are getting as much positive feedback as possible and very little negative feedback.

On the flip side, what gets resisted is less likely to get repeated. Every time you try to repeat a task and run into resistance, your brain says, "That wasn't very fun. Let's try to avoid that next time." So try to remove as much friction or negative feedback from this process as you can.

This reality makes it difficult to tackle those unfun tasks—unless, that is, we seek ways of generating positive feedback to help balance the scales.

Silly Tricks Actually Work

For many years before I knew I had ADHD, I struggled with doing basic household chores. I wanted to do them, but I just couldn't find the motivation to get it done. My house was a mess because I just continued to let things get out of control.

When I mentioned how frustrated I was about this to my friend Brian (who also had undiagnosed ADHD at the time), he nodded knowingly. He said he struggled with the same thing.

We realized one of the fundamental problems was that we just weren't getting any sort of positive reinforcement. Yes, doing the dishes and putting them away technically made our apartments cleaner and more attractive. But that sort of satisfaction was abstract and delayed. As we completed the chore, there was nothing immediate that screamed, "Great job, we should do that more often!" to our brain, so it was difficult to build up any sort of dish-cleaning routine.

I'm not saying this to complain or to ask you to pity two grown men who struggled with completing basic household chores. It's honestly kind of embarrassing to talk about this! My goal is just to tell you the truth. It felt like there was a blocker in my brain that made these silly little chores impossible to do.

Eventually, Brian and I came up with a plan to take matters into our own hands.

We both knew we really needed positive reinforcement to get stuff done. So we agreed to give each other just that by celebrating and encouraging each other whenever we did one of those mundane chores.

I would text him something like "Just did the dishes," and he would respond with "Heck yeah, nice work dude! You're crushing it! I'm doing mine now." I would respond to him in a similar way.

Then the cycle would repeat itself the next night.

It was silly, and you might think it wouldn't work because we were basically cheating our way into earning positive feedback.

But it *totally* worked! Even though it started off as kind of a joke, the "joke" evolved to become something essential: a good motivator. I started doing the dishes just to be able to say "hey, I did the dishes!" and I knew it encouraged him to do the same.

Turns out there really was something to our little account-ability system. Just a minor example of how embracing something that may seem a bit silly can be an effective motivation strategy.

MOTIVATION STRATEGY GUIDE

As we've discussed, finding the motivation to do important work is one of the major challenges for people with ADHD.

With that in mind, I'm concluding this chapter with a mini strategy guide. It's specifically designed to help people with ADHD find motivation to get work done and focus on the things they want to accomplish.

Remember that no ADHD strategy will be a magic bullet. What works amazingly for one person may not help someone else. A particular strategy might not help you at all but will be gold for a different reader. Or a different strategy might work perfectly at first and then lose its effect. The point is to 1) find a strategy that works in the moment and 2) mix things up as needed.

Consider the way a sports team uses a playbook. They have a comprehensive list of different strategies and a plan of attack. It's a great starting point for executing a play. But when a play is no longer effective, they adjust their strategy and try something else from the playbook.

Use the same approach with this strategy guide!

ADHD brains are fascinated by the new and novel, and repelled by the boring and ordinary. **So find the strategies that work for you, for now**.

When a strategy stops working—don't fret! Find a fresh approach, pick a new play. Remix it and make it uniquely yours.

These strategies are also meant to inspire your own. Think of this guide like a build-your-own-strategy toolkit. Customize it to your liking and grab what's necessary for whatever task you face.

If you're stuck on a task you can't seem to get started, flip through this section and try something new. Some may seem too obvious or simple—but often that's exactly what you need. A simple, well-worn path can be a convenient way to get where you need to be.

Strategy: Add Action Verbs to Tasks

We all know how difficult it can be to get started on a project. Sometimes you don't even realize you're stuck, so you waste time getting nothing accomplished. You can't seem to make any forward progress.

When you're stuck like this, set aside ten minutes or so to write down some concrete tasks. This may reveal that the tasks you're trying to accomplish aren't actionable. Or that other tasks need to be completed first, before you can get to the ones you had in mind.

Good tasks are verb-driven. Verbs = action. Here are some examples:

- ☐ *send* email to vendor
- ☐ *fill out* paperwork
- ☐ *wash* dishes

If you just write "taxes" as a task, it's hard to get started because you're omitting the actions required to complete the task. Once you try to come up with a verb for "taxes," though, you may find that other tasks reveal themselves.

For example, you can't "file taxes" until you enter your tax data. You can't "enter tax data" until you've collected all the paperwork. Thinking backward can help you figure out the tasks that need action first.

Thus the vague task of "taxes" might become:

- ☐ Gather all tax paperwork
- ☐ Log into tax website
- ☐ Enter tax data
- ☐ File taxes

This list lets you know what concrete actions you need to take. And by breaking the task into smaller chunks, it also gives you opportunities to get your momentum train in motion. Rather than sitting around thinking "I should do my taxes"—a vague, undefined assignment—you have something to work with.

Strategy: Break a Project into the First Couple of Steps

When you break a project into *all* of its steps, it can be really overwhelming. First you had a giant daunting project; now you have a giant daunting list of tasks.

So rather than building a massive list of work to do, focus on identifying the first few steps that you can act on now.

It's important to know your overall goal for the project. But once you're able to visualize it, you can turn your attention to the more modest (though no less essential) task of just getting started. Build that momentum. Once your motivation train has gained steam, you'll be able to figure out all the additional steps.

Here's a simple principle to keep in mind: when taking on large projects, focus on the fewest steps needed to take action.

Strategy: Change Your Environment

It's easy to get stuck in a rut where nothing seems to motivate you. Being surrounded by the same old scenery may be part of the problem. Changing your environment can be just the trick for making everything feel fresh again.

Try moving to a new room or working from a new desk. If possible, you could try working in a public area like a coffee shop or shared coworking space.

These places can sometimes be noisy, though, so make efforts to keep those distractions to a minimum. A coffee shop might be perfect with a pair of noise-canceling headphones—or it might be a dose of sensory overload that makes it impossible to get anything done.

Find What Works Best for You

If moving your location isn't an option, try updating your environment. Add something to your workspace like a new lamp, fresh plants, or a favorite guitar hung up on the wall. Open a window for fresh air or introduce a revitalizing scent with an aromatherapy diffuser. Try listening to a new genre of music.

With these simple changes, you may find a renewed sense of energy.

Get yourself out of a motivation rut by changing your current environment or finding a new one.

Strategy: Create Personal Challenges

Few things energize me more than someone telling me I can't do something. That sounds like a challenge, and I love beating a challenge.

Even if you don't think of yourself as a competitive person, you can still benefit from treating a task as a challenge. Here's how it works.

Get a notebook and label the cover "Stuff That's Too Hard" or "Things I Can't Do" and fill it with hard tasks you've been avoiding.

You won't always be in the mood to tackle something difficult. But when you're in the mood to take on a challenge, prove that notebook wrong by tackling something written inside and marking it off with a Sharpie.

The trick is to find that Goldilocks zone where the difficulty is just high enough to engage your interest. You want a challenge that feels almost out of reach, but not so difficult that you get frustrated and give up.

Create a personal challenges notebook to engage your competitive nature.

Strategy: Eat the Ice Cream First

Don't try to tackle your difficult tasks first—i.e., "eat the frog first." Instead, you should "eat the ice cream first."

Our motivation works differently than most neurotypical people, so focusing on the hardest task doesn't work. We just get stuck. We're a lot better off focusing on things that feel easy or fun to do instead.

Start with those "ice cream tasks" to build up your motivation momentum, and then move on to more difficult tasks once you're already on a roll.

Strategy: Embrace the Pivot

I used to spend entire weekends building up what I thought would be the perfect productivity system. Reminders, schedules, automated tasks, short-term and long-term goals; this system had it all, whether I was planning for today or ten years. This was going to be the perfect system.

At least, that's how it began. If you've also spent hours fine-tuning a "perfect" productivity system, you know things don't always work out like they're supposed to. Inevitably, something gums up the works.

Maybe you forget to check your task list one day, and the next, and the next until you forget it even exists. Or maybe a complication comes up, so instead of using your perfect system, you switch to writing tasks on an index card for the day. Or worse, you abandon the work you were supposed to get done to fix your productivity system instead.

Often, you simply grow bored with using it. At the start, it was fresh and new and exciting—but that initial novelty was only enough to power you through the building process. Once complete, your passion faded. With the novelty gone, you lost all your momentum.

And now your tasks and projects are trapped in a system you no longer have the energy to use.

Planning for the Pivot

There's no reason to feel bad about this. Your brain is built differently, and that's okay—embrace it! Knowing you will eventually grow bored with a system can even be seen as a gift. It means you can expect this issue from the start.

You can plan for the pivot.

Rather than building an elaborate system, keep it simple. You know you're going to need to pivot to a new system, so make an easy transfer your goal. Focus on keeping things uncomplicated.

There's no reason to build an entire cabin for a weekend camping trip. You know your stay is temporary, so you bring just enough to meet your needs for the weekend. And then you tear it all down when you're done.

In the same spirit, make your productivity system easy to tear down. Keep it simple so you can easily transfer tasks and projects. Build a minimal system without too much "magic" or automation (not because automation is bad, but because it can take a lot of time to set up and may be difficult to move to a new system). If it's a digital system, make sure you can easily export your data when it's time to move on.

Energy & Motivation Management

You might think moving your data from one system to another is a waste of time, but your primary concern isn't *time* management: it's *energy and motivation* management! If your system isn't working anymore, it's time to move on. Having all the time in the world won't help you if your tank of motivation is empty.

Embracing the pivot allows you to remain in control and not feel trapped by your own system.

The best part about this? You don't have to feel bad about trying the shiny new to-do app or trendy new productivity system (so long as it's simple!). We know novelty is motivating, so we're just embracing what works for us!

Plan for the pivot by accepting you will grow bored with most productivity systems/tools and be proactive about making your tasks easy to transfer to something new.

Strategy: Externalize the Problem

Sometimes you get stuck when you can't see an issue clearly. You trick yourself into thinking you fully understand the problem you're trying to solve. But there's something that isn't quite making sense, and you can't seem to make any progress.

When this happens, try to externalize whatever it is you're wrestling with. Get the details out of your head so you can examine them more fully.

Here are some quick tips for getting the most out of this strategy.

Write It Down

Pretend you're writing an email to a friend and explain the task, the steps involved, and what the result will be. Or sketch it out. It doesn't need to be fancy.

You can even use a napkin or scrap of paper to keep it from feeling too much like "work." The important thing is to make the problem visual.

Describe It Out loud

When you explain a problem out loud to someone else, sometimes you realize the solution in the process of explaining the problem.

This solution is so effective that in software development a process called "rubber duck debugging" has become an accepted best practice. It works like this: any time a developer is grappling with a thorny problem, they are expected to explain their problem to a rubber duck first (whether real or imagined).

Once said aloud, they often are able to solve the problem themselves, without bothering a busy coworker. And yes, many software developers have an actual rubber duck on their desk as a reminder to do this.

By externalizing your problem (i.e., getting it out of your head) you can often discover issues or gaps in knowledge you couldn't see before. Why not give it a try?

Strategy: Find a Body Double

Body doubling is a strange name for a strategy if you've never heard it before, but essentially it just means working in the presence of someone else.

As a kid, I could never keep a clean room (and to be honest, I'm not *that* much better as an adult). Whenever I tried to clean, I would get distracted by some nostalgic item I picked up, like an old poetry notebook, a photograph from years past, or some cards from a game I used to play. I just couldn't seem to get started and stick to it.

But sometimes, my mom would ask me to clean while I had a friend over. Suddenly, it seemed possible. The presence of someone else helped to propel me forward into getting work done.

How to Body Double

When you want to start body doubling, there's a simple model for how it works.

- Tell the other person what you plan to do for the session ("I'm going to work on a chapter outline in my book")
- Set a timer for a defined chunk of time (usually 30–60 minutes)
- Work quietly for the allotted time

- Share what you did at the end of the session ("I finished the outline and started writing my first rough draft")

That's it! Pretty simple. And surprisingly effective.

Just by announcing your intentions to another person, you create a sort of social contract that helps motivate you to get your work done. The best part: this is true even if they don't ask you about it at the end of the session or try to do anything to hold you accountable. Just their presence alone is often enough.

Body doubling can even be effective virtually, where the other person isn't in the same room but is just using video chat.

There are plenty of ways to find someone you can body double with:

- ask friends, family members, or coworkers
- join online communities that host body double sessions (even if they don't call them that)
- sign up for virtual coworking apps and services

Scheduling these body doubling or coworking sessions can help build a sense of routine and habit. It can also help you clarify your goals.

I find I will often sit down to work on something, only for hours to pass without me getting anything done because I haven't clearly defined what I should be doing. But since I need to tell someone else my intentions for a body doubling session—and I know they will ask how it went—participating in the process forces me to state my goal clearly and focus on it.

If you're ready to try body doubling, further encourage yourself to stay focused by naming a goal and setting a timer. Doing both while working in the presence of someone else significantly increases your odds of a productive, focused work session.

Strategy: Gamify It

When you're stuck doing a boring task like filing taxes or taking a test, try to turn it into a game to keep yourself engaged. It doesn't have to be complicated. Sometimes just putting a new spin on something can make it easier to complete.

For a test, options could include:

- answering every other question first
- starting at the end and going backward
- drawing a small doodle after every page is complete

You can also mix things up by adding some challenge and urgency to the task. How many questions can you answer in three minutes?

Make boring tasks into games to help you get them done quicker and with less resistance.

Strategy: Let Things Go

Whenever you think about a looming task or spot it on your to-do list, you're likely to feel stressed. This may mean you're adding stress to your life for weeks or months (or years).

In light of this, it's worth periodically reevaluating some of those tasks—and not being afraid to let them go when they're no longer truly necessary. Maybe you don't need to reorganize all your vinyl records in autobiographical order after all?

Maybe you're being haunted by a looming task that has no real deadline. One option to try: write it down on a folded piece of paper and drop it in a jar labeled "Someday, Maybe." This may help you let it go without stressing you out that you'll forget about it. After all, it's sitting there in the jar.

Sometimes, though, you can write that task on a piece of paper and toss it in the trash. You can't do everything. It's okay to decide that a task that once felt so important is no longer a priority.

Reevaluate older tasks to see if they are still important. Don't be afraid to let them go if they no longer match your life priorities.

Strategy: Make Chores Novel

As we've discussed, mundane chores can be kryptonite to the ADHD brain. They certainly are to mine.

There's no interest to be found in a boring, repetitive task like folding your laundry or vacuuming the stairs. But you can spice things up by creating novelty:

- Folding clothes in rainbow order (ROYGBIV: red, orange, yellow, green, blue, indigo, violet)
- Putting away the dishes in largest-to-smallest order
- Vacuuming every odd stair step first, then every even one

You might roll your eyes at these suggestions. I get it, they seem sort of silly or even childish. But seriously, these simple changes in your approach can help you transform a boring chore from drudgery to something fun and engaging. (Well, *more* fun and engaging at least.)

Strategy: Mode Shifting

Sometimes you will get stuck on a problem and nothing you do seems to work. You're just stuck.

When this happens, don't force yourself to stay focused and keep working. Take a break and engage in a new activity that's completely different.

Go take a walk, or maybe try playing a musical instrument. Can you juggle? Then juggle! You're looking for something that's going to engage a different part of your brain and help you shift into a different mode.

When you return to the troublesome task, it may feel fresh, or perhaps even novel.

Pay attention to when your brain gets stuck and your efforts seem to be a waste of time. Shift into a different type of activity to help reset.

Strategy: Race Against the Clock

Some of the most productive times in my life have been when I'm up against a deadline with a limited amount of time remaining (talk about a challenge!). That urgency can be particularly motivating for people with ADHD.

So make a deadline for yourself. Start a timer and give yourself a challenge to finish before the clock hits zero. Set a shorter time increment (fifteen minutes or less) to really amp up the urgency and crank out some quick work.

Challenge yourself to complete a task within a certain time limit.

Strategy: Start with a Ta-da! List

Creating a new to-do list can be intimidating. You usually start with a blank page and then fill it up with work you need to get done.

With a ta-da! list, you add items you've already accomplished for the day, big or small, work related and not.

Here's an example. Imagine you've been chipping away on a big, looming work project, but it still feels like you aren't making a lot of progress. To provide encouragement, you write down tasks you've completed so you can see that you really are getting stuff done.

Here are some things it might include:

- ☑ watered the plants
- ☑ took the dog for a walk
- ☑ brought the trash cans back from the curb
- ☑ replied to five emails
- ☑ called a client about next week's project

Maybe you're having a particularly difficult day, and it feels like you have nothing worth putting on the list. That's okay!

As far as I'm concerned, even the basics count:

- ☑ got fully dressed
- ☑ took a shower
- ☑ made coffee

The point of your ta-da! list isn't to impress anybody else, it's to help you build up momentum and feel that thrill of forward progress.

Once you have your ta-da! list, check those items off. Now that your list is helping you feel accomplished, it's a great time to start adding new tasks to be completed for the day (aka, to-dos).

Beginning with a ta-da! list is a small change that can make a big difference. When you look at a to-do list and most of the tasks are already checked off—even when they aren't necessarily monumental accomplishments—your perspective shifts. Everything else on the list feels just a bit easier to tackle.

Start with a ta-da! list by adding and checking off things you've already accomplished.

Strategy: Take Side Quests

In video games, "side quests" are smaller missions you can tackle that help you build up your character and level up so that it's easier to take on and defeat the main boss. This is also a great technique for tackling extensive projects in real life, especially when you don't seem to be making forward progress.

Rather than trying to just "get focused" on that primary task, find a related task that feels a bit more interesting or fun to tackle. Something to build up that momentum train. Even better if it gets you toward the ultimate goal.

Sometimes a large project or assignment might feel too daunting, but then you find an angle or aspect of the project that's especially interesting and draws you in. Suddenly, the rest of the project begins to flow naturally.

For example, I often get excited about new design projects because they give me an excuse to explore a new technique I've been meaning to try. This is true whether or not I'm initially excited by the project itself. By wiggling my way in through the side, I create momentum to tackle the bigger task.

Be careful though: sometimes side quests can become an entire project on their own and distract you from your primary mission. Use timers as regular check-in points. Set a countdown timer for, say, twenty minutes to make sure you're not spending too much time wandering aimlessly down another path.

When the timer finishes, ask yourself, "Do I want to continue this side quest, or am I leveled up enough to get back to the main path?"

Find side quests that can propel you forward when you're stuck and create momentum toward your goal.

Strategy: Use Audio as a Distraction (and a Reward)

Find an album, podcast, or audiobook that you really want to listen to, perhaps something related to your latest hobby or obsession. Then restrict yourself so you can only listen to it while doing a specific chore or activity.

This restriction does double duty for you. One, it helps motivate you to start an activity with an immediately interesting reward. And two, it gives your brain that highly sought-after extra stimulation. Now you have something interesting to focus on while completing a mundane task.

Personally, I always wear headphones when doing chores.

Even though it takes only a minute or two to take out the trash, I'll pull out the headphones and listen to a bit of a podcast.

Why? I know if I don't do this, eventually the mundanity of that chore will feel overwhelming. I'll end the task thinking "That was not fun" rather than being distracted by some interesting podcast I'm listening to.

Once it becomes difficult to start doing a chore, you may just avoid it forever.

Tackle boring chores with the immediate reward and distraction of listening to something interesting.

TIME

The Clockless Mind

When I was in school, the same scenario would play out over and over again. Whenever I got a large assignment, it was like I was in a game of chicken with the deadline. I would wait until the night before it was due to complete—and often I didn't even start it until then! Even with the deadline looming, I would continue putting it off until late into the night.

It didn't matter what the subject was. Whether I was interested in it or not, I would put it off and put it off.

But at some point—usually past midnight—something in my brain would finally click into urgency mode. The deadline finally felt near, and I would jump into frantic, focused action.

I knew it was too late to give the assignment the time it deserved, and my mind raced in desperation to get it complete. And I would! Usually. The urgency of the moment would often give me just the push I needed.

Last-minute panic, my muse.

People with ADHD have a complicated relationship with time. We don't seem to perceive it the same way as most neurotypical people.

As a concept, time makes sense. We think we understand it. But in practice, it becomes unclear, and the minutes, hours, and days often blend together.

It's like we don't have any internal clock or sense of time. We have a clockless mind. We only seem to understand two states: the present ("now"), and some vague version of all future time ("not now").

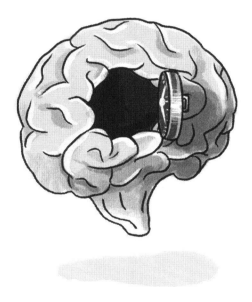

To illustrate what this looks like, let's do a quick thought experiment. Pretend you're in school and have a large assignment to complete. It's going to take a lot of work to finish. How do you feel about its urgency in the time leading up to its due date? If you're like me, or many other people with ADHD, it looks a bit like this:

- **Five weeks out**
  More than a month away is "not now," so you put the assignment off or ignore it and forget about it. You might think, "I have plenty of time to do this later" without really considering how much work is required or how much time you *actually* have available.

- **Five days out**
  This is still "not now." You might start to worry about it, but it still feels like it's a problem for future you to deal with.

- **Five hours out**
  Uh oh, you start to feel that "now" is imminent. Your urgency flares up and suddenly it's time to fly into action. And fly into action you do.

- **Five minutes out**
  It's time for panic mode! "Now" has arrived and you frantically work up to (and often past) the deadline in an attempt to finish the remaining work on time.

Time Estimation

A 2023 review on ADHD and time perception shows that people with ADHD have significant difficulties with time estimation.[3] Probably not surprisingly, this can have a massive impact on our daily professional and personal lives. Under these conditions, it becomes difficult to maintain any sort of future schedule or manage expectations for future work.

I know I've always struggled with estimating how long it will take to complete projects or tasks. Sometimes I will avoid a task for weeks or months because the time commitment *seems* significant. But when I finally tackle the task, such as cleaning out my car, it might take less than twenty minutes rather than the several hours I was expecting. I probably should have just done it and moved on.

Years ago, I worked as a freelance web designer. One of my biggest struggles was figuring out what to charge for a new project. When trying to estimate how long a project would take, I never really knew if it was closer to five hours or fifty. This was further complicated because I was early in my career and often worried that my proposed budget would be too much. I constantly underbid myself, thinking I could do everything in much less time than was realistic.

When I blew past my expected number of billable hours, I would work late nights trying to catch up and make up for time I didn't have.

These difficulties with time estimation can also lead to chronic procrastination.

I often said yes to exciting new projects or opportunities but then left them for "future Jesse" to deal with. It always felt like somehow, I would have more time tomorrow. But there was one problem: "future Jesse" is me! And I never seemed to have that magic extra time.

By kicking the can down the road, I was just building up the amount of work I would eventually have to deal with.

ADHD Burnout

Since people with ADHD struggle with estimating time, they don't hear the internal warnings neurotypical people do when they procrastinate and put things off. There's no alarm shouting, "There's not enough time for this later!" You end up with a growing list of looming tasks—snoozed obligations you procrastinated on and large projects you underestimated—until they come due simultaneously, sending you into panic mode.

Burnout is often the result when your overcommitting catches up to you and becomes overwhelming. One day you're on top of the world—then suddenly everything seems to fall apart at once.

It becomes a recurring cycle. You commit to doing something that interests you or that you're skilled at. Then another opportunity comes along, and you jump on board for that too. Then you commit to another thing, and another, and another.

I've often had the bad habit of saying yes to things if I have the *ability* to do them—but without considering whether I have the time, energy, or motivation to do so.

Sometimes I feel like I'm juggling chainsaws by constantly adding these new commitments. Juggling chainsaws is exciting, sure, and it gets even more thrilling as you add more chainsaws. And this excitement can definitely trigger that novelty-based motivation too!

But eventually we get overwhelmed by all these commitments. Fatigue sets in. It's not a pretty sight watching all those chainsaws come crashing down at once.

Strategies for Managing the Clockless Mind and Avoiding Burnout

Difficulties with time perception and time management can often lead us to the brink of burnout (or beyond it, to the abyss below). To avoid this, it's important to develop strategies to help you keep track of time more effectively and manage your future commitments. Here are some strategies for getting that done.

LEARN TO SAY NO GRACEFULLY

It's so easy to say yes to things when they sound like exciting opportunities. Since you don't have that "not enough time!" alarm bell, however, this inclination gets you into trouble.

Pick your battles wisely and don't agree to everything. Give yourself more time to consider commitments. Consult your calendar, or a friend who knows you well, to make sure you aren't putting too much on your plate.

Instead of agreeing to every new opportunity or request that comes your way, here are a few things you can say instead:

- "I'd love to, but I need to check my schedule."
- "I can't now, but maybe next time!"
- "Oh, that sounds fun. When do you need to know by? I don't want to overbook myself."
- "Let me make sure I have the time to give this my full attention."

We often default to saying yes in the moment, only to later regret it when it's too late to back out (and you remember all your other commitments and deadlines). That regret often leads to panic and overwhelm.

René Brooks says you should "guard your yes with your life."[4] Stay strong and intentionally start with "no" as your default answer. Refuse to agree to every single new opportunity that comes your way. I know how hard it can be, especially when a new and exciting opportunity drops in your lap. But if you don't have the time . . . well, you don't have the time.

CREATE TIME-BASED GOALS RATHER THAN OUTCOME-BASED ONES

When you have ADHD, estimating time can be a struggle because of your clockless mind. Sometimes you overestimate, sometimes underestimate. But time never seems to work quite how you expect it to.

Rather than beat yourself up about it, adapt your workflow to use what works better for your brain.

Stop using outcome-based goals, which are typically framed like this:

- "I'm going to finish writing this paper today."
- "I'm going to clean the entire office this weekend."
- "I'm going to do my taxes tonight."

These types of goals set you up for failure because your estimates often aren't accurate. Then you get frustrated with your lack of progress, which further demotivates you.

Instead, use time-based goals:

- "I'm going to write for one hour."
- "I'm going to clean for twenty minutes."
- "I'm going to work on my taxes until 8 p.m."

When you do these tasks, enter them in a time log. In the future, rather than guessing at how long a task will take, you can just look at your history. Over time, you'll have an excellent base of data you can draw from to improve your estimation skills.

MAKE MICRO-COMMITMENTS

For someone with ADHD, even simple activities can feel too daunting to start. A boring task like washing dishes can seem like it will take hours.

What you need to do is make the task look ridiculously easy. Don't commit to washing all the dishes. Just commit to washing three dishes. Or even a single dish.

- Your office is a mess? Commit to cleaning two items off the desk.
- Trying to work out more? Commit to doing two push-ups, or even just changing into workout clothes.

That's it.

Once you get started, you often end up doing a lot more. But even if you don't, taking that micro-step is taking a (micro) step in the right direction!

Propel yourself into motion by making a micro-commitment—a fast and easy way for making progress.

USE VISUAL TIMERS

One of the simplest and most effective strategies for staying focused is to use a visual timer. When I'm working, I almost always have one counting down.

Since we struggle to perceive time conceptually, a visual timer helps us by making time something physical that we can see. As the timer counts down, we can see the visual representation of time getting smaller, helping us feel the movement of time.

This can help activate the **Complete** motivator from the 4 Cs, making us feel some urgency and helping to build up that momentum. The visual progress of a shrinking line drives a sense of urgency that gets you moving.

I particularly recommend the Pomodoro Technique. This is when you set a timer for twenty-five minutes of work and follow it with five minutes of rest. Do this three to four times in a row, then take a longer break.

The 25/5 ratio isn't a hard and fast rule though; use whatever spread works for you! I like longer work sessions (and longer breaks), so I might do forty minutes on, twenty minutes off.

For my daughter, we mix in the **Create** motivator and use a more generous helping of rest. She does eight minutes of homework, then draws cartoon dogs for her eight minutes of rest.

The important thing isn't necessarily to stop when the timer ends, but to decide whether to continue. When I'm working with a countdown, I get into that hyperfocus zone, and the timer reminds me of the passing of time. If the timer goes off and I'm not ready for a break, I just reset it, skipping the break to go for another forty minutes.

Either way, I'm in control. Without the timer, three hours might go by with me helplessly jumping from one thing to the next or getting sucked into a single task for way too long. I don't get to choose how to spend that time. A visual timer gives you back control with a soft nudge to your hyperfocus.

If you find that you're skipping breaks and regretting it later, set up rules beforehand! Add a sticky note to the timer that says, "Must stop!" or maybe even a checkbox next to the phrase "I took my break."

Even taking a quick moment to stretch your legs, get a glass of water, visit the restroom, or refill your coffee can be enough to help you re-center and recharge.

You can also use the **Compete** motivator by giving yourself challenges.

- How many words can you write in twenty minutes?
- Can you answer every other question before time runs out?
- Maybe you can finish the entire task early for an extra-long break.

Use visual timers to keep your time management on track and to generate urgency that will motivate you.

Always Late or Always Early, Never on Time

While writing this book, I taught some of the material in a live online course on ADHD. A little while before the course started, as I was preparing, I looked at my video and noticed that my background seemed just a bit off-balance. I decided I needed a plant to complete the look.

Luckily for me, I just so happened to have seen the perfect one at a nearby store just a few weeks ago. It was a tall plant, so I wouldn't even need a table or anything to put it on.

I check the clock—one hour until the course starts. "Plenty of time," I tell myself. "I can even grab some coffee and a quick bite to eat while I'm out."

The store is a quick drive, less than ten minutes away. But as soon as I get inside, I discover the tall plant I want is gone. Shoot. I spend some time surveying the options, and eventually settle on a smaller plant that has the right vibe.

Perfect! Now all I need is a little table to put the plant on . . .

Sometime later, I walk toward the cash registers with my plant, a small table, a cool little lamp, and some new pens. I see that there's a line—a big one. I suddenly remember that time exists and check my watch: the course starts in thirty minutes. Oh nooooo. Panic sets in.

After what feels like an eternity, I get through the line and dash to my car with fifteen minutes until start time. You might think I was relieved to see I could get home in time with five minutes to spare. But you'd be wrong.

What I saw instead was an opportunity to squeeze in a quick coffee run . . .

There's a good chance this harrowing saga is all too relatable. People with ADHD often struggle with being on time to things because we have a fuzzy grasp of time itself. This often makes us late to anything and everything with a set time. (Others with ADHD may have learned to overcompensate, arriving early to everything because they are terrified of that feeling of being late.)

Whenever I'm about to leave the house for an appointment or meeting, more often than not my brain will suddenly come up with five things that I need to do "real quick." Are these things important or needed before I leave? Usually not. But I find myself trying to get them done anyway.

My brain will tell me lies like "You can make it up on the way" and "Maybe you'll hit every green light?" I'll also conveniently forget about the time it takes to park a car. Or find the building. Or that traffic is a thing that exists.

It's as if my brain feels the urgency of a pending appointment and thinks, "Hey, this urgent energy is motivating—we need to use this to get something else done!" So I frantically work on random tasks, only to arrive late to a commitment with no good excuse.

It doesn't even matter how important the appointment is! I've been late for job interviews because I decided I had time to sort mail or respond to an email I've been ignoring for weeks before leaving the house.

Others with ADHD will have the opposite problem, always arriving exceedingly early instead.

Sometimes this is learned behavior or even a response to trauma after years of getting in trouble for being late. You think, "I need to do whatever it takes to not be late, even if that means showing up forty minutes early."

For others, it may be because of overcompensation—anxiety takes over and your fear of being exposed as "a late person" drives you to be the first to arrive.

If your life often feels out of control, arriving extremely early can feel like one way to regain your autonomy.

Waiting Mode

Another issue that affects late-to-everything and early-to-everything ADHDers alike is Waiting Mode.

When you have an afternoon meeting or appointment, you may find it impossible to concentrate on anything else. You're stuck in Waiting Mode. It's almost like rumination; you find that no matter what you try to focus on, you can't stop thinking about the pending meeting. You're trapped in executive dysfunction and unable to focus on anything else.

Under these circumstances, the early-to-everything people may choose to arrive early because they feel like they can't get anything done anyway. Late-to-everything people might feel similar at first, but when a sense of urgency hits, they suddenly try to accomplish a flurry of things—making them late again (as usual).

Strategies for Avoiding Chronic Lateness and Waiting Mode

Even if you've been a "late person" for longer than you can remember, it's not too late to improve. Here are some easy tips for getting a better handle on your time.

KEEP A HISTORICAL TIME LOG

Use a stopwatch or timer app to record how long it takes you to get somewhere. Make a guess before you leave and then compare it with how long it actually takes. Start the timer the moment you leave the house and keep it going until you've completely arrived (i.e., not just pulling into the parking lot).

When you get a time, write it down in a log or in the Notes app on your phone—any place you can quickly reference in the future to help you better estimate how long the journey *really* takes.

Be sure to consider all the steps that are required as part of the travel process.

- Are you planning to get coffee, fuel up your vehicle, or run another errand on the way?
- Are you leaving at a time of day when there's likely to be more traffic?
- How long will it take to park? To walk from the parking space to your destination?

- Is the location on a higher floor that requires an elevator? Do you need to be checked in at a front desk?

Remember that all these extras (parking, walking, and finding the location within the building) are part of your time calculation. Recording every step gives you a realistic number to refer to the next time you need to complete the same trip.

TURN WAITING MODE INTO THINKING MODE

When you're stuck in Waiting Mode, one productive way to channel your nervous energy is to journal about what's on your mind. Free-write about the meeting or event you're waiting for and write down anything you're worried about or overthinking.

You may find that once you see these worries written down, Waiting Mode fades some and your attention is drawn elsewhere. (This has been my experience, at least.)

DO SOMETHING FUN

If you know that you'll be stuck in a long period of Waiting Mode, accept that you probably won't be able to accomplish anything "important." The upside is that this can free you up to do something fun or interesting instead. Trying and failing to do something important won't break you out of Waiting Mode, so embrace the opportunity to enjoy yourself.

Explore a hobby, read an interesting article, go for a walk, or talk with a coworker. Sometimes, this can even help you build up the motivation and focus you need to work on something important.

But set an alarm (or three) so you don't miss the original task you're waiting to do!

Is Urgent the Same as Important?

People often confuse importance and urgency, especially those of us who struggle with distorted time perception.

Important tasks have long-term impact and move us toward long-term goals. Examples include developing a new skill, building relationships, or working on a big work project. These often don't have an immediate deadline but are crucial for long-term growth and success.

Urgent tasks often show up unexpectedly and feel like they need to be done right away, regardless of their long-term impact. Examples include rushing to complete a project before a fast-approaching deadline, fulfilling a pressing request from your boss, fixing something that just broke, responding to some sort of emergency, etc.

An enormous project due in forty days is important.

But *anything* due in forty minutes feels urgent.

The problem is that the energy of an *urgent* task can make it feel like an *important* task. Our brain prioritizes the now over the future. Urgent tasks push their way to the top of our to-do list and push out those things that are actually important.

When something is urgent, it demands immediate attention. The *gotta-do-it-now-or-it-will-be-too-late* feeling masks the fact that what's grabbing our attention probably isn't actually very important (and, in fact, may push us further away from our long-term goals). We're drawn into the grip of last-minute panic.

Since people with ADHD are particularly motivated by this urgency rather than importance, we must find other ways to prioritize important tasks so they don't get left behind.

Strategies for Prioritizing Importance Over Urgency

It's easy to get bogged down by urgent tasks that always seem to pop up. It's key to remember not all urgent tasks are actually important. Here are some strategies to help you prioritize importance over urgency so you can make the most of your time.

MAKE IT OBVIOUS

When a big project or task has a distant due date, it's easy to forget about it until the urgency kicks in. Whenever you have an important task, write the deadline somewhere where you will see it and in a large, easily readable font. Good options include:

- a whiteboard
- sticky notes
- your screensaver or phone background

Anything that is visual and catches your eye will help bring that important task to the forefront of your brain. Sometimes, those obvious visuals can blend in with your surroundings, so take the time to spice them up: move sticky notes around to new areas, add little doodles to the whiteboard around your reminder, etc.

Make important tasks obvious and visible so that you don't forget about them until the last minute.

SET UP REMINDERS

Another great way to track those important tasks and deadlines is by setting reminders for yourself. These will prompt you about any looming deadlines and help you prioritize tasks you are more likely to forget in the day-to-day chaos of your life.

Here are a few easy ways to make sure you're reminded:

- **Set up recurring alarms.** If you have tasks that need to be completed at regular intervals, consider setting up an alarm on your phone or computer to remind you to take action.
- **Schedule emails to yourself.** If you check your email regularly, you can schedule an email to show up in your inbox at a certain time. You could use this strategy for a specific reminder, or to keep a recurring list of things you want to be reminded of. For example, you could schedule it to be delivered every Monday morning to start your week.

- **Use a reminder app.** There are some great mobile apps for tracking reminders, and most phones even have native reminder apps. I prefer apps that let you easily snooze a reminder. This way I can't make the mistake of marking it complete and making the notification go away—only to forget to act on the reminder. I keep a strict rule with reminders to never mark them as complete until they are actually complete. If you find that you're ignoring certain reminders, remove them! Don't compromise the reminders that are still working. Re-assess why you're ignoring certain ones and find another approach.

- **Ask a partner or friend.** If you're lucky enough to have a partner or friend in your life who's great with time and memory, ask if they would be willing to help you remember an important upcoming event. This works great as a backup system. Be careful not to abuse this opportunity or take them for granted, however—and be lavish with your appreciation when they help you remember something important.

These are just a few ways you can set up reminders. You just need a system that will display reminders without you having to remember to look at them, reminding you something important is coming up soon.

Summary of Time Strategies

Learn to say no gracefully: Avoid overcommitting by "guarding your yes" and not agreeing to every new opportunity.

Create time-based goals rather than outcome-based ones: Use time-based goals, rather than outcome-based ones, so you can celebrate success even when you don't completely finish a task in the time you have available.

Make micro-commitments: Propel yourself into motion by making a micro-commitment—a fast and easy action to ensure progress.

Use visual timers: Use visual timers to keep you on track as time passes and to generate urgency that will help get you (or keep you) motivated.

Keep a historical time log: Use a stopwatch or timer app to record your travel times to make better estimates in the future.

Turn Waiting Mode into Thinking Mode: When stuck in Waiting Mode, write out your thoughts to help clarify your thinking and clear any worries.

Do something fun: Alternatively, when you're stuck in Waiting Mode, try to embrace doing something fun instead of just worrying and doing nothing at all.

Make it obvious: Make important tasks obvious and visible so you don't forget about them until the last minute.

Set up reminders: Create reminders to help you keep track of important tasks.

MEMORY

Out of Sight, Out of Mind

People with ADHD are often surrounded by piles of clutter. My desk is in a perpetual state of chaos, covered in piles of books, papers, index cards, and random other things I don't want to forget. Even my digital world often gets overtaken with "piles" in the form of open apps, cluttered notes, and browser tabs—oh so many open browser tabs.

People with ADHD are often juggling lots of different projects and hobbies (or "chainsaws"), and more projects and more hobbies means more piles. Piles across the desk, piles on the floor, piles in every corner of the room (rather, *rooms*). Or maybe you keep a tidy desk and office space, but also use your car as extra closet and storage space.

Why is this so common for people with ADHD?

This kind of hoarding is actually a form of self-preservation. Why? Because we often forget things we can't see.

Instinctively, you know this. When things are truly put away—hidden in the depths of a box or drawer—they disappear from your brain entirely. This is why planners never seem to work for people with ADHD. The second you close the cover, you forget everything inside. Without a routine in place, you might never remember to open it again.

When I was younger, sometimes my mom got so fed up with the disastrous state of my bedroom, she would clean it herself. I hated when she did this! (I bet she did too.)

"How will I ever find anything?!" I thought.

It may have seemed like chaos to her eyes, but for me, it was organized chaos.

When things are "a mess," they are out in the open and I can use them as some sort of physical memory palace; the placement of each item reminds me where they are. It may look like a mess, but I can find exactly what I'm looking for.

This difficulty with forgetting about things you don't see can extend beyond just knick-knacks on a desk.

Sometimes I might forget to do something that's part of my regular routine. Maybe I had a change to my routine and forgot to do something that I always do—possibly an important work responsibility. Now it's fallen out of my brain, no longer part of my environment or schedule.

When this happens, I might never remember that thing again unless something specifically reminds me. It's as if it fell into one of those boxes or drawers I never remember to open.

This phenomenon can occur with people, too. If you haven't seen someone recently, you might forget to invest time in maintaining that relationship and may even forget they exist until you see them again in person. This can add a lot of stress to personal and family relationships. Other people are often offended and fail to understand what's happening.

Strategies for Keeping Things Top of Mind

When things pile up, important tasks or intentions can disappear in the noise. Here are some strategies to help you stay on track and keep those important things from getting lost.

GET A (GOOD) APP

Phones can be a huge distraction, but they also have lots of apps and tools to help us manage our organization (as discussed in the previous chapter).

The key is to find apps that work with you.

For reminders, I prefer an app that will nag me repeatedly until I tell it "Okay, okay, I did the thing!" but you might prefer something different. If you are more of a visual person, it might be important to choose an app with a pleasing design, so you enjoy the experience of using the app.

You can even set up recurring reminders to check in with a friend. That might seem silly to some, but if it helps you maintain a friendship you might otherwise forget, it's not silly.

There are also a lot of different types of notetaking apps that can help us organize our thoughts and ideas (so many ideas!). This organization can feel freeing when we realize we don't have to remember everything. Try to stick to a single app for this so you never have to go hunting for whatever app has the business plan for your brilliant Airbnb-for-penguins startup idea.

One of the biggest problems to be aware of when relying on your phone is notification overload. Notifications on notifications on notifications.

These can easily become overwhelming, so it helps if you start from zero by turning off all but the most important notifications. You want a notification to be a signal for action, not just more noise you easily swipe away to ignore. Fortunately, many newer phones have focus modes that can help you better manage notifications.

Using apps and tools with customizable notifications can help you manage your organization and stay on top of your tasks and responsibilities.

MAKE IT CONVENIENT

The best way to make something easy to do or remember is to make it super convenient.

If you want to remember to take your medication every day, place it next to your toothbrush or coffee maker—somewhere you'll see it every day—so you'll have a visual cue to help you remember to take it. (Bonus tip for medication: use a timer cap or day-of-the-week pill organizer so you don't forget if you've taken it already today.)

Or if you're tired of your forgotten veggies going bad, follow the advice of KC Davis and place them in the open areas of your fridge so you see them every time you open the door.[5] You can move soda or condiments to the drawers. You'll have no problem digging to find those, so it's fine to make them a little less convenient and obvious.

Make important reminders and information more convenient, visible, and easily accessible so you're more likely to remember them.

Remembering to Remember

Before I knew I had ADHD, my wife and I had fallen into an unhealthy pattern that reoccurred almost every single night.

In the evening, my wife would ask me to take out the trash. I would tell her something like, "Sure, Babe," planning to take care of it as soon as it was time to get ready for bed. And every single night, I would get up from the couch, turn off the lights, walk right past the garbage can, and head straight to bed without taking out the trash.

I had no idea I was doing this.

When my wife asked me to take out the trash, I *meant* it when I said "Sure." My plan was truly to take out the trash. It was a simple chore, and I intended to take care of it before I went to bed.

But somewhere in the time between me saying "Sure" and me walking past the trash can, that intention seemed to have faded away.

What made things worse is that it looked like I was just being lazy and inconsiderate.

My actions communicated to my wife that I just didn't care—that I was trying to avoid doing the work and simply giving her an answer I wasn't planning to follow through on.

It didn't matter that I had good intentions. I wasn't following through.

It was a tremendous strain on our marriage, and at the time I barely even recognized the issue.

It turns out I struggled with prospective memory. Prospective memory is essentially "remembering to remember," or remembering later to do something you planned to do. Here are some examples:

- "I should grab milk on my way home tonight."
- "I'll call Emma back in the morning."
- "I can take out the trash before I go to bed."

Your prospective memory helps you remember to act when "later" comes.

The relationship between ADHD and poor prospective memory was well demonstrated in a 2019 study in the Netherlands. As part of the study, participants were asked to write a list of their intentions: things they planned to do that week. Things they would need to remember to act on later.

Subjects, who included people with and without ADHD, were supposed to call the researchers several days later to check in. The goal was to see if they remembered what their intentions were and if they had acted on them.

More than half of the ADHD participants forgot to even call—a noteworthy (and not too surprising) finding in and of itself. When this happened, a researcher called them instead. Once they were on the phone, it became clear that the participants with ADHD were more likely to have forgotten what their intentions were and, as a result, failed to act on them.[6]

The reason people with ADHD often struggle with following through on goals we set isn't because we "lack willpower" or aren't trying hard enough. We're often trying much harder than most. The problem is that our brain chemistry makes it harder for us to remember these things we're trying to work on. We forget to remember what we set out to do.

So, when we invest time learning some novel approach for productivity, a new tool or technique to help us get stuff done, we have great intentions for how this is going to help us. We believe we are going to use this new system and it may be just the thing to solve our problems. But inevitably our intentions fade from memory, and we forget about using this tried-and-true approach without even realizing it.

Or maybe you intend to cultivate a useful new habit; say, writing down your weekly tasks and then checking them every morning to assess your progress. But morning comes and your prospective memory doesn't remind you to check the list. Eventually, you may forget the list of tasks even exists.

Here's an example of how this played out in my life. As I was writing this book, I worked on an elaborate plan for my launch. I had a calendar highlighting when things needed to be done, a list of podcasts I wanted to schedule interviews for, plans for developing a launch team, tips for contacting media and helping spread the word, and a list of additional strategies I wanted to try out.

The only reason I can now tell you about this elaborate plan is because I recently stumbled onto it when clearing out some browser tabs that had been open for over a year. (Yes, I know.) I'd completely forgotten I made this plan, and it was too late to take advantage of many of the good ideas I had written down.

Our best intentions often seem to be temporary. We find it difficult to remember those things we intend to do. Lost in that space between thinking and acting.

Strategies for Remembering to Remember

Even if you struggle with prospective memory, the good news is that there is a lot you can do to overcome this. Here are some simple strategies for helping you remember those important tasks and deadlines.

MAKE IT VISUAL

Remember my issue with forgetting to take out the trash every night?

After I was diagnosed with ADHD, this came up in therapy. Our therapist was familiar with the difficulties of prospective memory and recommended we hang a whiteboard in a prominent location in our house, somewhere I would walk by on my way to getting ready for bed.

From then on, my wife would ask me to take out the trash as before, but she also wrote "take out the trash" on the whiteboard as a reminder.

That whiteboard became a physical representation of my intention to take out the trash, as well as a visual reminder. I saw it as soon as I was heading to bed, and I was never annoyed to see the task. In fact, I was almost delighted. "Oh yeah, I said I would take care of the trash!"

That seemingly "minor" change made a major difference in my life. It helped me remember what I had intended to do. It helped me keep my promise.

Since we hung that whiteboard, I've never forgotten the trash again. Eventually it became so ingrained in my nightly routine (like turning out the lights and setting the alarm) that I didn't even need the written reminders anymore.

Keeping important things visible and in your line of sight will 1) help you remember future deadlines and 2) remind you to act on them. Here are a few simple ideas for doing this:

- Write reminders on sticky notes or index cards. Make sure they're placed somewhere you'll easily see them again.
- Hang a wall calendar or whiteboard on a wall you often walk by and use it for important dates, notes, or reminders. Mix up the colors and revise it frequently so it doesn't just become background visual noise.
- Use a screensaver or digital photo album to remind you of friends and family you should stay in contact with.

Make your prospective memory visual by keeping important reminders and information in your sights. Once you do this, you'll be far more likely to remember and act on them.

CREATE AN ACTION ANCHOR

Another helpful remembering strategy is to use an anchoring object. The purpose of this object is simple: to help you remember an action you intend to take. The key is to place this anchor near the location where you want to remember to act.

Examples could include:

- putting workout clothes or equipment near the door to remind you to go to the gym
- placing an empty medication bottle in your car to remind you to pick up a new prescription
- setting an empty watering can near your plants to remind you to water them

Sometimes even a random object can do the trick if it's something that stands out as unique. I'll sometimes put something random in my pocket, like one of my kids' toys, as a reminder to do something unrelated like call my friend back or some other activity I don't want to forget.

Customize your anchors as needed. Whatever it takes!

Working Memory

People with ADHD often have a more limited working memory, the short-term memory you use to track information for tasks and cognitive activities.

I like to think of working memory like a shelf that holds the information I'm currently keeping track of. When we gather some data that's relevant, we put it up on the shelf. But when you have ADHD, we have more limited shelf space. So, as we put things on the shelf, we are more likely to push other things off.

Distractions can be even worse, since they can knock *everything* off the shelf. That distraction gives you something new to remember for the moment, pushing out an important thought you've been trying to hang on to.

A quick interruption can derail you for hours. It can cause you to disengage completely from what you're supposed to be doing, since you're afraid all your work may come crashing down again with each new interruption.

You might even lose the plot in a movie, book, or conversation. This can lead to mind-wandering and confusion. Once you've lost the thread, there's no point in trying to track what follows.

For example, maybe you go through the same ritual I do when I cook something like mac and cheese. I grab the box, glance at the instructions, and think the details are stored:

- "Okay, boil for eight minutes."
  Toss the box in the trash.
- "Wait, was it eight minutes or twelve?"
  Retrieve the box for another look.
- "Right, eight!"
  Toss.
- "..."
  Retrieve the box again.

I still do this whenever I'm cooking. I fool myself into believing my working memory is magically going to work this time. But it never seems to.

This also means important details can disappear without being noticed. With no reference to check, you might start a project with all the confidence in the world, unaware of some important bit of information you've lost. Some steps may be forgotten or done in the wrong order.

Or you might overcorrect from past mistakes. Once you get stuck, you may be afraid to act unless everything is clearly defined and written down. This mindset doesn't exactly encourage creativity or adventure.

Strategies for Better Memory Management

Rather than get frustrated with our memory difficulties, let's look at some tools and strategies that will help us remember to remember.

DOUBLE-CHECKING BEATS REWORKING

When someone is giving you a task or responsibility, take the time to double-check the details to make sure you've got them right. Repeat the instructions back to them by saying, "What I hear you saying is . . ." or write what you think their expectations are and ask them to confirm.

People miscommunicate all the time! It's worth the effort to make sure that you're on the same page. Don't waste time working on something that ultimately doesn't match what's expected.

An added benefit of double-checking is that it can often reveal potential difficulties before you're too far down the road. Sometimes the act of asking for clarification will reveal gaps in your understanding and lead to important new questions.

Double-check your assumptions about a project or task to ensure you fully understand the requirements and expectations.

MAKE IT PERMANENT

Make a record of things so they can't be lost.

Don't tell yourself, "I'll remember this, it's important." Write it down so you have something to reference. Carry a notebook and pen around with you if it's feasible. Make it a habit to write down details when you get them.

If you're meeting someone on a video call, consider recording the meeting for future reference (with the other person's permission, of course!). There are even apps that automatically transcribe video calls so you have a searchable record of your conversation.

You've likely forgotten important things in the past, so learn from that history. Do you detect any patterns? If so, how can you interrupt the cycle?

All of which is to say: write it down, refer to it, make it visual and permanent.

USE DROP ZONES AND LAUNCH PADS

Have you ever left the house in a rush, only to realize you forgot your keys, wallet, or something else important? Or maybe you didn't forget anything, but you just can't seem to remember where everything is.

In the past I've thought, "I'll put this somewhere weird, so I'll remember it's there." But when it's time to go and I need the item, it's nowhere to be found! It's still right where I put it. I just can't remember where that is.

Instead of putting it somewhere "weird" or "safe" (aka somewhere new each time), designate a specific area near your front door to keep everything you need when you leave the house. This area can be an end table, a basket, a tray, or anything else that can hold what you need.

This is where you will store your wallet, keys, purse, or whatever your daily carries are. When you enter the house, drop those essentials inside so they are ready for launch.

Remember that this is for essentials, not an extra junk drawer. When it's time to go, you don't want to think about which things to grab and which to leave behind. The point of a launch pad is that it has all the essentials ready to go and you don't need to make any decisions. Just grab everything in the launch pad and take it with you.

Be strict with yourself: don't put your launchpad items anywhere else in the house. These have one destination, and that's where they stay when you're in the house.

Yes, that even includes the place you think you'll "definitely remember" but never seem to recall.

COUNT ON IT

Another memory technique is to associate numbers with a group of tasks or actions to help you remember all the things you need to do. This helps build habits and routines, and, ultimately, helps establish a normal rhythm for your tasks.

For example, let's say every night before you go to bed, you have to complete four tasks. When it's time to go to bed, you'd literally say "Bedtime, four" out loud to remind yourself about the four things you need to do. Here's how it works:

"Bedtime, four."

1. lock doors
2. turn off lights
3. set alarm
4. brush teeth

You can also count down with your fingers as you complete each action. Anything you can externalize from your brain will make it easier for you to stay focused and follow through on your intention.

Here's what you could say when it's time to leave your house:

"Leave house, three."

1. Check for phone
2. Check for wallet
3. Check for keys

You can use this in combination with launch pads too. Say out loud, "Leave house, three," to make sure your three items are on the launch pad and you're ready to go. You could even put the number on the launch pad itself for an easy reminder.

To build a routine, name it and its associated number of tasks out loud. This will help you recall a group of required actions that you'd have trouble remembering on their own.

Summary of Memory Strategies

Get a (good) app: Using apps and tools with customizable notifications can help you manage your organization and stay on top of your tasks and responsibilities.

Make it convenient: Make important information convenient, visible, and easily accessible so they are more likely to be remembered.

Make it visual: Keep important reminders literally in your sights so you're more likely to remember and act on them.

Create an action anchor: Use action anchors, objects associated with an action you want to take, as environmental cues to complete a task.

Double-checking beats reworking: Double-check your assumptions about a project or task to ensure you fully understand the requirements and expectations.

Make it permanent: Create a permanent record by writing things down so you can reference your notes in the future.

Use drop zones and launch pads: Use launch pads placed in consistently used drop zones to store essential items and ensure you don't forget to bring them with you.

Count on it: To build a routine, name it and its associated number of tasks—then say both out loud to recall the required actions.

EMOTION

Success Amnesia

For most neurotypical people, past success can serve as motivation and inspiration for future success. But because people with ADHD have a weaker memory, we rarely use—much less benefit from—hindsight.

This means we tend to discount or forget our past wins. They fade quickly into the fog of time.

That's not all. While you may have trouble remembering many of the nice things people have said about you or the impressive things you've accomplished, your selective memory *does* hang on tightly to past mistakes. Every failure makes a permanent imprint that overshadows the few wins you can recall.

Fleeting success, lasting failure.

This diminished hindsight can make you feel like a failure, focused as you are on negativity and unaware of your own strengths and qualifications.

Most people experience negativity bias to some degree, but it can be particularly severe for those with ADHD. Their brain is more likely to "learn" from negative events, leading them to make future decisions based more on avoiding negative situations that occurred in the past than on the merits.

Making matters worse, for most people with ADHD, there is an abundance of negative events in the past to "learn" from. Harvard psychiatrist Michael S. Jellinek has estimated that children with ADHD may receive 20,000 more corrective or negative comments than their peers by the age of ten.[7]

It can be overwhelming to think about all the things you've learned to avoid. It's hard not to fixate on the failures that seem to dominate your story.

Imposter Syndrome

People with ADHD often experience imposter syndrome as well. After a lifetime of hearing you aren't doing things the right way, you might feel like a fraud—worried you aren't qualified to be in the position you're in and living in fear you'll be exposed.

Imposter syndrome is compounded for people with ADHD because we have a hard time remembering our successes.

Even if we do remember them, we often dismiss and discount them by comparing them to our biggest failures. Or you might think, "That was too easy for me, so it doesn't count."

This combination of poor memory, past failures, and sensitivity to negative feedback pulls you down into self-doubt. You can't remember what you've done well, but the memories of when you've failed or disappointed people remain strong.

If you're not conscious of it, you can easily get stuck ruminating in this negative headspace. You need to find an escape.

Strategies for Overcoming Success Amnesia and Imposter Syndrome

Success amnesia and imposter syndrome can be major hurdles that create difficulties in many areas of our lives. They can lead us to lose trust in ourselves and hamper our chances to succeed.

Given these stakes, it's worth acquainting yourself with strategies that can help you overcome both by building more confidence in your abilities.

CREATE A SMILE FILE

This negative headspace can become a permanent internal soundtrack that plays on an endless loop, breaking our self-worth and self-confidence. It's difficult to turn this soundtrack off.

That's where a smile file can help. To get one started, set aside twenty minutes to think of any past successes and write them down. Start with thinking about the past week or past month, then the past year, etc.

Don't worry about whether an accomplishment will impress other people. These are the things that are a personal win for you, no one else. Something you are personally proud of, even if others might not understand.

Maybe it's a positive performance review at work or successfully launching a project you've been working on for months. Or maybe you remembered to call a friend, finally answered some emails you've been avoiding, or got out of bed on a difficult day. What counts as "success" so often depends on our current life circumstances.

You can even ask people you trust for honest positive feedback and write it down. Or maybe someone left a nice comment on social media or sent you a supportive email; save a screenshot or write it down in a notebook. This kind of encouragement can be rocket fuel to the ADHD brain.

The goal is to have a list of these accomplishments, compliments, and any other wins that make you smile when you see them. You should remain on the lookout for new smile moments to add so you can build up your smile file collection.

Once you have these down, set a recurring reminder so you remember to read them. You might be surprised by how

much a quick glance at them can spark a shift in your mood
and motivation.

Whenever you're feeling that negativity or imposter
syndrome, refer to this smile file to remind yourself of the
things your hindsight lets you forget. These wins and victo-
ries can bring positivity and encouragement back to your
daily life. Replace that worn-out negativity soundtrack with
something that brings a grin to your face and some lightness
to your spirit.

Living with Emotional Intensity

Life with ADHD can be intense. **Really intense.**

We can experience high highs and low lows—everything seems to be an extreme. And we're often unaware that what we are experiencing is any different from how others react.

You assume everyone experiences these things at the same intense level that you do: excitement, fear, pain, joy, distress, panic. In fact, you're often surprised and confused when people think you're being "a bit much" when it's just the way you naturally act.

It doesn't make sense. Why aren't others responding in the same way? Don't they also experience these intense feelings?

When it comes to emotions, most neurotypical people have an accelerator pedal and a brake pedal. They can gradually speed things up or slow them down as needed. Whether it's their emotional level, how excited they are, how angry they are, sometimes even the way they experience some types of pain. Occasionally, in an extreme situation, they might need to slam on a pedal. But typically, there's a gradual rise and fall between these states. There is control.

People with ADHD rarely have these control pedals. Mostly we just have a turbo button. And an inconsistent one to boot.

It seems to go off at random times, sending us full speed in whichever direction we happen to be facing, putting our emotions into overdrive.

Suddenly you're shouting for joy—or the tears have started flowing. Out of nowhere, your emotions are suddenly at maximum speed. Extreme situations seem commonplace, yet no less extreme, despite their frequency. It can feel like you're completely out of control.

This reality is personal. I've lost jobs after some minor conflict set me off to full speed.

In each case, the situation seemed far more intense in the moment than it does in retrospect, and I reacted to the intensity that I felt. Often the "conflict" was just a misunderstanding or a boss trying to understand why something happened, but it felt like an attack, and my emotional intensity smashed that turbo button.

"Blowing things out of proportion" was commonplace for me, and it felt like I had no choice. My actions felt instinctual.

It really wasn't until I learned about my ADHD that I began to get better control over my emotional responses.

In the past, my reactions felt justified. They were proportionate to how I *felt* those emotions. Strong reactions became just part of who I was, and it felt pointless to try and change that.

Through therapy, I was given tools to see my emotions in a new light. The emotions themselves weren't the problem. The emotions I felt were valid.

The problem was that I often misinterpreted what I was feeling and why I was feeling it. I jumped to conclusions about what emotion I should be feeling and immediately hit that emotion at full speed.

In other words, my understanding of emotions was simplistic and flawed.

Building Emotional Intelligence

To better understand why people with ADHD respond to emotions with such intensity, we need to better understand those emotions themselves. Let's take a quick look at what emotions are and how they work.

The human brain is always guessing and predicting what is going to happen next. It's like we're creating a weather forecast in our mind, constantly updating and making adjustments and corrections as we gather new data.

This forecasting actually causes physical changes in your body. For example, you might start sweating before giving a work presentation, since your brain predicts that you'll feel nervous in the spotlight. Or as you're waiting for a comedian to walk out on stage, you discover you're already smiling in anticipation of the joy and laughter you're about to experience. Or you tighten your grip on your steering wheel when it starts to rain, your mind now considering slick roads, limited visibility, and erratic drivers.

These changes happen naturally without us thinking about them. It's the basic formula of emotion: our brain makes a prediction, identifies that we will likely feel a certain way, and turns on the systems in our body that are associated with that emotion.

- If we anticipate happiness, our bodies often relax. We may smile or laugh and even feel an extra jolt of energy.
- If we anticipate sadness, our bodies feel heavy. We avoid eye contact, lower our heads, and may get teary-eyed. There's a loss of energy. We might feel a lump in our throat.
- If we anticipate anger, we often feel tightness in our bodies. We clench our teeth and fists. Our heart rate and breathing rate both increase. We might adopt a more aggressive stance and even feel blood rushing in our ears.

Because people with ADHD feel things so strongly, our brains often make the wrong prediction. The intensity level of our response does not match the gravity of the situation.

So when we experience a minor conflict, say a disagreement with our boss, our brain mistakenly sees it as a *major* conflict and sets things in motion. Our body gears up for a fight when it should have chilled out. Because we are so agitated, we provoke a much more serious and emotionally charged response—which seems to justify our overreaction in the first place. This is the definition of a negative, self-fulfilling prophecy.

We need to help our brain make better predictions with our emotions once those chemicals get flowing.

One way you can do this is by expanding your emotional knowledge base to give your brain more information to use for these predictions. Rather than having a simple emotional vocabulary of a few options (happy, angry, sad), we want to dial in a more nuanced understanding with additional labels.

Here's an example of what this looks like. My friend Vada gets quite irritable when she hasn't eaten in a while. When this happens, she likes to joke about it, saying, "Sorry, I'm Hangry Vada right now" ("hangry" being a portmanteau of "hungry" and "angry"). Though it may seem trivial, her announcement actually has a lot of power: it both defuses the situation with a humorous label and helps her recognize that what she's feeling isn't *genuine* anger.

Labels like this can really help to articulate more complex feelings and help us better understand what we're going through. When you label an emotion and give it a name, you start to recognize patterns. You can even embrace silly labels like "Hangry Vada" to help slow down intense emotions by calling light-hearted attention to it.

If you're often getting into disagreements with your boss that you tend to blow up to something big, maybe you could tell yourself "Alright, no need to be Drama Llama here!" The goal isn't to belittle yourself or mock how you feel—it's to help give you a moment to pause, recognize the emotion, and then choose a healthier response to the situation.

Strategies for Managing Emotional Intensity

The intensity of emotions people with ADHD experience can be a blessing and a curse. Feeling immense joy over even the little things can be wonderful! Overreacting in anger? Not as much. Here are some strategies to help you manage and better understand your emotions.

EXPAND YOUR VOCABULARY OF EMOTIONS

Besides creating silly names for common situations, you can teach your brain to be better at labeling all of your emotions more precisely.

The best way to do this it to build your own vocabulary of emotions. As you learn new ways to describe and label your emotions, you open new pathways in your brain. These additional details let you take more appropriate action—even if it's simply to do nothing rather than respond out of instinct.

If you look online you can find emotion wheels: visual aids that display a range of emotions that fit under an umbrella label ("angry," "sad," etc.). But I think building up your own vocabulary from scratch is more valuable.

To do this, start out by writing ten different words to describe the emotion of feeling sad.

Example: depressed, gloomy, worried, uneasy, crappy, frustrated, mournful, distressed, miserable, downhearted, etc.

Now go through those words and define what makes them different. What is the difference between "downhearted" and "gloomy"? What about "uneasy" vs. "mournful"? Take the time to come up with unique definitions for each of these words.

Try to rank them on a scale of intensity of emotion. Which of these implies the strongest feeling? The weakest? Play with these names and give them weight and individual meaning.

If this is a struggle, another option is to try associating a memory with an emotion. Maybe you can recall a time that you felt downhearted, and a different time where you felt gloomy. This adds weight to those emotions and can help you pick apart the minor differences between them.

Now write ten words to describe the different states of being "happy." Repeat this for "angry," and so on.

These exercises can help you discern how you feel with more precision. And that can lead to better solutions. Maybe when you're downhearted, a comforting cure is to listen to some sad music and drink hot cocoa. But when you're distressed or mournful, you need to talk with a close friend.

Learning these nuances can make a big difference in how you deal with emotions when they strike.

Expand your vocabulary of emotions to better understand the nuances in emotional states and improve how you respond to them.

USE A MOOD JOURNAL

A mood journal or mood tracking app can be a valuable tool for better understanding and managing your feelings long term. It involves documenting any emotions, thoughts, and experiences you have throughout your day.

By doing this, you'll be able to identify trigger-and-response patterns as they come up in your daily life. Understanding which triggers influence your mood can be invaluable when it comes to self-discovery and provide a personal roadmap for better anticipating and dealing with negative emotions.

You can use digital tools and apps for tracking mood, or just keep a mood journal at your desk that you write in every day.

Here's what keeping a mood journal might look like:

- **Write how you're feeling every day**, ideally around the same time. Try to be specific. Avoid using general words like "good" or "bad" but label specific emotions: anxious, frustrated, excited, content, etc. You can also rate your day using a scale of one to ten.
- **Note any significant events** or other factors that might be affecting your mood: people you recently interacted with, sleep/eating habits, events at work, the current weather, etc.
- **Reflect on your entries** at least once a week. Try to set up a routine of looking over the past week: maybe every Sunday night before bed, or first thing Monday morning. Look for any patterns and triggers (negative or positive) that often lead to similar moods.

Once you've documented a fair amount of information, you can use the journal or app to make adjustments in your life based on what you've learned. Spend more time with people or activities that improve your mood. Develop strategies to help you better cope with or manage negative triggers.

You can also use this journal to celebrate any positive changes you make over time. It's another way to help educate yourself about yourself—areas in need of improvement *and* areas to be proud of.

Rejection Sensitivity

One emotion that strikes people with ADHD deeply is the feeling of rejection or criticism. Our response to it can often be—stop me if you've heard this before—quite extreme.

Seemingly out of nowhere, you suddenly feel so deeply insulted, so betrayed, so hurt that you don't even know what to do with yourself. Many erupt and lash out in anger or desperation. Others may burst into tears or bottle everything inside, seeming to shut down completely.

When this happens, you don't even have time to think. The effect is so sudden that you only react to the sharp strike of rejection.

To those who don't know what's happening, your responses may seem confusing or inexplicable. They might say things like:

- "You have such a short fuse."
- "You're too sensitive."
- "You always get worked up over nothing."

If someone consistently reacts with such extreme feelings, they may be experiencing a form of emotional dysregulation often called Rejection Sensitive Dysphoria, or RSD. This term, introduced by Dr. William Dodson, speaks to the strong emotional response that can be triggered by a sense of rejection or withdrawal of love. This feeling can be so profound that it sends you to a state of intense negative emotion, even panic.

While RSD is not an officially recognized condition you can be diagnosed with, many in the ADHD community (myself included) strongly identify with its characterization of our experience, so the term continues to resonate.

When you have ADHD and feel like you're being rejected, that feeling cuts deep to your core and you respond in kind. Often your reaction seems over-the-top and too extreme to most, but it matches the intensity of how you feel internally. The reaction is intense because the feeling is intense! For some, this rejection can feel like actual pain.

This leads some to become people-pleasers or overachievers. You are terrified of feeling that rejection again, so you focus all your energy on trying to build up a bulletproof façade that can never be rejected or criticized. Or you may avoid putting yourself in social situations just to avoid any opportunity for you to be seen in a negative light.

The feeling of RSD can also present itself as a type of social phobia. You stop doing things you love. You abandon personal goals. Your world becomes a lot smaller.

Strategies for Handling Rejection More Productively

While we can't just turn off the intensity of rejection sensitivity, we can learn how to better respond when it happens. Here are some strategies for managing rejection sensitivity.

CREATE SOME SPACE

Fortunately, the feeling of Rejection Sensitive Dysphoria—though extremely intense—often fades quickly. So during an episode, one helpful thing you can do is try to remind yourself that it will pass. The best way to do this is by identifying and labeling the RSD.

In the past, I've actually said out loud to the person I felt rejection from, "I am feeling extremely angry right now, but I think this is the Rejection Sensitive Dysphoria. Can we take a break and come back to this in twenty minutes?"

I said this through gritted teeth, because the anger was REAL. The feeling inside me was authentic and intense! But as time passed, I could eventually see that the source of that emotion, the thing the other person said, was not as extreme as I thought at the moment.

Creating space can help you gain a better perspective on the situation.

REMEMBER THE PAST RELATIONSHIP

When you have a strong or unsettling reaction to something someone says, another useful strategy is to remind yourself of your history with this person.

Ask yourself:

- "Does it make sense, given my history with this person, that they would purposefully betray me the way I feel betrayed right now?"
- "Do I trust this person?"
- "Are they just having a bad day?"
- "Am I just having a bad day?"

I often find that past evidence shows me this person is not trying to cause me pain. It helps to assume the best of intentions for most people—especially those whom we've had long, positive relationships with.

This doesn't make your experience at the moment any less real or any less painful. But it can help you regain proper perspective (notice a pattern here?) and understand that the other person's *intention* was not to cause you that pain.

When conflict arises with another person, take a step back and compare it with your relationship history, checking to see if your worst interpretation really makes sense. (Hint: it probably doesn't.)

How Shame Distorts the Mind

People with ADHD are often crushed by the weight of shame.

The result of falling short of others' expectations for years, shame can persist daily, ready to strike at any point when you make some minor mistake, say the wrong thing, or forget an important detail. When it does strike, you think, "If only I'd tried harder this wouldn't have happened."

Growing up, you couldn't explain why you often seemed to mess up in the eyes of those around you. But it seemed to keep happening. Eventually, you started apologizing for things that weren't your fault. You internalized the blame from those mistakes you didn't even know you were making.

You might have heard harsh accusations like:

- "Why did you do it like that?"
- "What is wrong with you?"
- "Are you stupid or something?"

Maybe you still hear them. Or maybe, even if they're long gone, they reappear in your memory just to tear you down again.

The shame that these voices bring is especially brutal because it leads us further down a path of loneliness. We often blame ourselves for the pain we feel, so we try to hide it from others, afraid of further pain.

Left alone with our thoughts, we become even more prone to dwell on negativity and ultimately self-sabotage. When any small thing goes wrong, the result is all too familiar: we are sent down a negative shame spiral, compounding each thought with more and more negativity that builds up to an avalanche of self-doubt:

"I made a mistake."
"That was stupid."
"I always make this mistake."
"Why am I such a failure?"
"They're going to say I'm stupid."
"I probably am stupid."
"Maybe I should quit."
"I'm worthless anyway."

The shame spiral is swirling with lies. It says you are a burden, or you don't deserve happiness. Imposter syndrome shows up again, this time in overdrive, and you ignore any evidence to the contrary (i.e., reality).

Even when we acknowledge the truth of what's really happening, we can all too easily slip back into that shame spiral whenever something goes wrong. It can be sparked from a small word or even just a look. Squinted eyes that seem to say, "What is wrong with you?" can send you spiraling in an instant.

It feels like familiar territory that is difficult to avoid. Fortunately, though, there are ways out.

Strategies to Escape the Shame Spiral

FIND YOUR RESET

When the shame spiral takes over, it can be overwhelming. We lose sense of who we are. It attacks our very identity.

You need to find a way to reset—to center yourself back into remembering who you really are.

One way to do this is to seek experiences that refresh your emotional strength. Mindfulness, yoga, meditation, taking a bath, taking a walk, playing with a pet, hugging a friend, reading a book, etc.

The solution will be unique to you. Nostalgic experiences can often be a powerful way to re-center yourself. Maybe you watched 90s action movies with your dad when you were younger, or maybe spending time tending to a garden makes you feel whole again.

Find those experiences that recharge your self-worth.

WRITE OUT YOUR THOUGHTS AND FEELINGS

Taking the time to put your feelings into words can often soften the blow of a spiral and provide you with much-needed clarity and truth about your situation. This doesn't have to be formal or complicated; just grab a notebook and spend twenty minutes free writing.

Search for the lies your inner voice might tell you. It's easy to just believe everything that you hear inside your head, but putting those words down on paper lets you step back and evaluate things more objectively, as a kind of observer. It can help you identify those negative soundtracks you're keeping on repeat, reminding you it's time to turn the dial.

TAKE CARE OF YOUR BASIC NEEDS

When life is busy, it's easy to forget that we need to take care of ourselves. Neglecting our basic needs can compound negative feelings and lead us that much more quickly down a shame spiral. It's important to check in with yourself to make sure you aren't falling behind in these basic areas.

Drink plenty of water, shower regularly, get enough physical activity, eat nutritious meals, and get adequate rest. Though they may seem basic—and they are—these actions have an oversized impact on how you feel, and they are easy to neglect if you aren't careful.

Taking care of basic needs is crucial for your mental health and improving your overall well-being.

Impulsivity and Inhibition

Many people with ADHD find themselves driven by impulse.

You act rashly, leap before you look, buy what you can't afford, and make commitments when you have a full schedule. You make snap decisions and regret them later.

We do all of this because in the moment we can't foresee the consequences of these actions. They don't feel rash or foolish; they feel necessary. There's an urgency to them. But our diminished sense of hindsight means we often make these decisions without enough data. We're so quick to move into action, we don't truly consider how similar situations have worked out in the past.

Difficulties with memory and time already affect your hindsight and foresight. But when you suffer from impulsivity, you often make things worse by acting so fast you don't even let whatever limited hindsight and foresight you *do* have weigh into your decisions.

You sabotage your future self without realizing it through regrettable choices and commitments that can't be changed or undone.

Strategies for Managing Impulsivity

Our impulses can and often do get us into trouble. Here are some strategies to manage them better so you can make more deliberate and thoughtful choices.

BUY YOURSELF SOME TIME

Resisting an impulse to respond or act is extremely difficult. So instead of trying to resist it directly, you'll often be better off buying yourself time instead. You can do this by giving yourself an alternate action to take. This will give your hindsight and foresight a chance to catch up and weigh in more productively to the situation.

When you feel a strong emotional response bubbling up, instead of responding directly, try to say something like "Hmm, let me think about that" or even "Give me a minute to consider." You can even physically move your hand over your mouth, as if you're thinking about your response.

The goal is to redirect your impulse, pointing the energy away from a negative, emotionally driven response.

LEARN FROM PAST MISTAKES

When you have the space to do so, try to remember what's happened in this sort of situation before. Often when you act on impulse and do something regrettable, you end up thinking, "Why do I always do this to myself?" or "Ugh, gotta clean up the mess and apologize, again."

Obviously, taking a pause to recall how things ended last time is much easier said than done. But it's still worth trying to ask yourself, even in the face of (great) resistance, "Has something like this happened before? How did I respond? What was the result? Should I do something different this time?"

Experiment with a fresh approach and a new response to a situation until you find what works best for you. If it stops working, begin again.

Summary of Emotion Strategies

Create a smile file: Create a smile file of wins and accomplishments you can refer to, replacing your negative soundtrack with indisputable proof of your achievements.

Expand your vocabulary of emotions: Expand your vocabulary of emotions to better understand the nuances of each emotion and improve how you respond to them.

Use a mood journal: Using a journal or app to track and reflect on changes in your mood can help you better understand what's happening in your life and foster emotional growth.

Create some space: Creating space can help you gain a healthier perspective on a stressful situation.

Remember the past relationship: When conflict arises with someone, take a step back. Compare your history with the person to see if your strong immediate reaction really makes sense.

Find your reset: Find those experiences that recharge your self-worth.

Write out your thoughts and feelings: Journaling can provide clarity and help you identify negative thought patterns by allowing you to observe your emotions from a more critical distance.

Take care of your basic needs: Taking care of basic needs is crucial for your mental health and overall well-being.

Buy yourself some time: Resist impulsive reactions by buying time, which will allow your hindsight and foresight to catch up and weigh in on your decision-making.

Learn from past mistakes: Reflect on past situations to avoid making the same mistakes.

THE FUTURE OF ADHD

Despite the challenges I've outlined in this book, I'm convinced that the future is bright for people with ADHD.

As our understanding of the disorder improves and more people with undiagnosed ADHD get a proper diagnosis, the world seems to be shifting its perspective. There is growing acceptance of the importance of neurodiversity, the idea that there are a wide range of different brains with unique strengths and abilities.

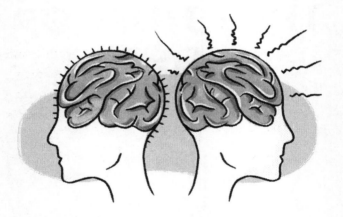

Traditionally, the field of ADHD research has mostly been deficit-focused, exploring what is "wrong" with people that have ADHD and how the "disorder" can be corrected. Today, however, many ADHD researchers are interested in strengths-based approaches and finding the positives of having ADHD.[8] We are seeing more people embrace it as a unique and positive way of thinking and being, challenges notwithstanding.

It all begins, though, with awareness. When you understand how your brain works, you can use that knowledge to your advantage. You can lean into your strengths and find ways to be more productive, creative, and successful in your personal and professional life.

It takes time and effort to reframe your thinking this way, but you've already taken the first step by reading this book. You now have a better understanding of ADHD and how it affects your life. And you have knowledge and strategies you can use to make positive changes in your life.

I know ADHD can be hard and frustrating and overwhelming at times. It can feel like the weight of the world is holding you down and your brain just won't act the way you want it to. But it's important to know what you're going through is not your fault. You aren't lazy or stupid or selfish. You simply have a brain that works in a different way. A brain that can do incredible things once you understand how to work with it.

Remember that you have the power to be part of someone's story and be the change you want to see. You can be an advocate for ADHD and neurodiversity, helping others to appreciate their brain and embrace both the strengths and challenges they face. You can be that role model, the person who is living a better life with ADHD.

The future for people with ADHD is hopeful.

Will you be a part of that future?

Final Notes

Thank you for reading this book. I hope it helped you better understand yourself or someone you love. If you found this book helpful, spread the word!

It would mean so much to me if you could leave a review. This helps others find the book and know it's worth their time. Thank you in advance!

Go to **extrafocusbook.com/review** to offer your thoughts.

Another great way to help others is to share this book. Post a photo on social media, tell your friends and family, or buy a copy to pass on to someone you think it will help.

If you have questions or feedback, positive or negative, I'd love to hear it. Contact me at **jesse@adhdjesse.com**.

Thanks again!

Jesse J. Anderson

ENDNOTES

1   A. Brzezińska, M. Borowiecka, M. Zając, K. Warchoł, and W. Michniak, "ADHD in women - a review," *Journal of Education, Health and Sport* 11, no. 9 (September 2021): 491–496. http://dx.doi.org/10.12775/JEHS.2021.11.09.063.

2   Jessica McCabe is an ADHD advocate, creator of the YouTube channel *How to ADHD*, and author of *How to ADHD: An Insider's Guide to Working with Your Brain (Not Against It)*.

3   Christian Mette, "Time Perception in Adult ADHD: Findings from a Decade–A Review," *International Journal of Environmental Research and Public Health 20*, no. 4 (February 2023): 3098. https://doi.org/10.3390/ijerph20043098.

4   René Brooks is an ADHD advocate, speaker, and creator of *Black Girl, Lost Keys*, a blog that empowers black women with ADHD and shows them how to live well with the disorder.

5   KC Davis is a licensed professional counselor, speaker, mental health advocate, and author of *How to Keep House While Drowning*.

6   Mareike Altgassen, Anouk Scheres, and Marc-Andreas Edel, "Prospective memory (partially) mediates the link between ADHD symptoms and procrastination," *ADHD Attention Deficit and Hyperactivity Disorders* 11 (2019): 59–71. doi:10.1007/s12402-018-0273-x.

7   This is not based on a study, but rather is a plausible estimate by Michael S. Jellinek, MD, a professor of psychiatry and pediatrics at Harvard Medical School. The estimate assumes that a child with ADHD may hear a negative or corrective statement from a teacher an average of three times an hour during school hours.

8   Jessica Agnew-Blais and Giorgia Michelini, "Taking stock of the present and looking to the future of ADHD research: a commentary on Sonuga-Barke et al. (2023)," *Journal of Child Psychology and Psychiatry* 64, no. 4 (April 2023): 533–536. https://doi.org/10.1111/jcpp.13758.

ACKNOWLEDGMENTS

I want to thank my children—Vera, Calvin, and Maverick—for reminding me that life is supposed to be fun and weird and full of joy. And an enormous thank you to my wife, Danielle, for the love and much-needed stability she brings to our fun, weird family.

Thanks to my editor, Adam Rosen, for taking my mess of words and making me sound more better (note: this section was not seen by my editor). And thanks to my illustrator, Nate Kadlac, for helping bring this book to life visually.

Thanks to my parents for doing their best to raise a bunch of kids with ADHD—I now understand how difficult that can be. And thanks to my wife's parents for their support and generosity.

Thanks to Brandon Jeffries for being the best friend I needed to survive junior high, high school, and beyond.

Thank you to Freda Carda, for helping me relearn how to walk after discovering I had ADHD, and for calling me out when I needed to be called out.

Thank you to the many members of the online ADHD and creator communities that have welcomed me and made this world of content creation a bit more welcome, and ultimately led to this book being made. Specific thanks to Andrew Nalband, Anna David, Aravind Balla, Barbara Luther, Becca Kerber, Ben Putano, Brittany S Hochstetler, Brooke Schnittman, Carolee Flatley, Casey Neistat, Celz Alejandro, Chenell Basilio, Chris Achard, Chris Scott, Christian Genco, Claire Twomey, Connor DeWolfe, Courtney Carini, Damon Manley, Dani Donovan, Daniel Bustamante, David Sparks, Deniz Perry, Derek Sivers, Dickie Bush, Dusty Chipura, Dylan Redekop, Eric Tivers, Esther Nagle, Ev Chapman, Hannah Hobbs, Ian Tomlinson, Jay Miller, Jaye Lin, Jennifer Anderson, Jennifer Farley, Jens Lennartsson, Jeremy Finck, Jeremy Ginn, Jessica McCabe, Jon Surratt, Julia Mullins, Julia Saxena, Justin Lai, Karaminder Ghuman, Kate Brownfield, Katie Hughes, Kevin Shen, Khe Hy, Kyla Roma,

Leah Leaves, Leanne Maskell, Leo Mascaro, Lindsay Guentzel, Marie Ng, Marie Poulin, Marc Koenig, Meredith Carder, Michele Hansen, Mikah Sargent, Mike Schmitz, Monica Lim, Natalia Peña, Nicolas Cole, Nicole Bulsara, Nik Nieblas, Olivia Silvana, Päivi Butcher, Paulina Riviere, Pina Varnel, Rach Idowu, René Brooks, Rich Burroughs, Rob Fitzpatrick, Ron Capalbo, Rosie Sherry, Ryan Mayer, Samantha Demers, Samantha Postman, Sangeet Kar, Scotty Jackson, Shannon Craver, Sharon Pope, Stephen Scott, Sylvester McNutt III, Tammy Burdick, Tina Mathams, Tish Gentile, Todd Ellis, Tracy Winchell, Trina Haynes, Yina Huang, and many more.

Thank you to my early beta readers which helped shape the book into what it is today. This book will help more people, thanks to your early feedback and support! Specific thanks to AJ Harman, Aleksey Tentler, Andrea Karlin, Anthony Farruggia, Billy Adams, Brad Niskanen, Carla Carducci, Cathy Buck West, Cyndee Mitchell, David Cameron, Enrique del Perpetuo Socorro Marín García, Fara Grim, Guide Fari, J. Adam Hoving, Jens Hillmann, Joey Harris, Kate Farah, Kelly Berry, Kenny Whitelaw-Jones, LaTeisha Moore, Lexi Webster, Linda Eskin, Maria Neubauer, Martha Rubiano, María del Rocío Varela Martín, Matthew B Brandabur, Michael Pichan, Milo Frazier, Paula Cayuela Vela, Puja Teli, Reanna Szeszol, Rohan Gayen, Ryan Bradford, Sam Purgavie, Sneha Jha, Tré Ammatuna, Tushar Joshi, Victoria Penn, and more.

Thanks to anyone else I forgot. If you think you should've been in here, you're probably right. Oops.

And finally, thanks to Ms. Myking, who believed in me.

About the Author

JESSE J. ANDERSON currently lives in Puyallup, WA with his wife and three children. He wears multiple hats as a writer, speaker, coach, ADHD advocate, and maker of things.

Diagnosed at 36, Jesse writes about his insights and experiences living with ADHD in the weekly newsletter, *Extra Focus* (**extrafocus.com**), helping countless readers navigate their own ADHD journeys or better understand their loved ones. He is known for his humorous, relatable, and insightful posts about ADHD under the handle @adhdjesse, and has been featured in publications including *Today* and *Huff Post*.

He is still trying to reach his "potential," but writing this book is a good start. If you find his driver's license in this book, please return it.

Looking for weekly advice on living smarter with ADHD?

Visit **extrafocus.com** to join the Extra Focus newsletter.

Printed in Great Britain
by Amazon

47753216R00101